CANDIDATE
FOR TRUTH

By Sybil Norton and John Cournos

PILGRIMAGE TO FREEDOM:

The Story of Roger Williams

FOR

CANDIDATE TRUTH:

The Story of Daniel Webster

by SYBIL NORTON
and JOHN COURNOS

Illustrated by RUS ANDERSON

HENRY HOLT AND COMPANY · NEW YORK

For

Marcia Small Satterthwaite

granddaughter of William Henry Kurtz
and
great-granddaughter of Christian Caius Kestner
both lawyers and both candidates for truth

CONTENTS

CHAPTER ONE

A COTTON HANDKERCHIEF

W̶E THE PEOPLE OF THE UNITED STATES . . ."
A small, slight boy with brilliant black eyes, jet-black hair, and a swarthy complexion, was doubled up on a low stool, reading the words printed on a cotton handkerchief. The candle flickered on his determined finger which followed the printed words.

Young Daniel Webster was snug and warm in his homespun suit, as he sat beside the fire reading and watching his mother and younger sister Sally prepare supper.

At the turn of the nineteenth century Salisbury, New Hampshire, where the Websters lived on the banks of the Merrimac River, was a sparsely settled, sprawling township, one of the last on the road to Canada.

> "Lift up your heart! lift up your voice!
> Rejoice, again I say, rejoice!"

His mother's full contralto voice was echoed by little

Sally's piping tones. Sally was the youngest of the ten children. She was blue-eyed and fair-haired like all the Websters who had come from Scotland over a hundred years before. Only Daniel, his brother Ezekiel, and his father were dark and swarthy; all the other children were blond and tanned by years spent in farm work. They were famous in their county for their skill in farming and their common sense. Daniel's father and Ezekiel were six-footers, too, and handsome men. Only little Daniel was puny.

". . . in Order to form a more perfect Union . . ." Daniel's black eyes shone as he studied the words on the handkerchief.

Suddenly the door burst open, letting in a gust of icy wind. Covered with sleet and snow, his brother Ezekiel flung his coat and coonskin cap on a long bench.

"Hello, Ma," he greeted his parent who, at the sound of the opening door, had begun to take the food from the stove.

He lifted young Sally high in the air and gave her a resounding kiss.

"Sweet as sugar, ain't she, Daniel?" he said as the laughing child rejoined her mother.

As Ezekiel came over to his brother, his expression softened. A special bond of love had united these two younger boys from their earliest years. Although Ezekiel was double Daniel in size, he was not quite two years older.

"You still spelling out that old pocket handkerchief? It's only the Constitution. You don't want to spoil your sight over that tiny print."

Daniel raised shining eyes to his brother. "But listen, Zeke," he urged with enthusiasm. "It says 'in Order to form a more perfect Union, establish Justice . . .'"

"I know all that. Father's often told us."

"But I never *read* it before," protested Daniel.

"No, probably you didn't, but what does that matter? You read the Bible, too, but it doesn't make it any truer than when our minister preaches."

Daniel smiled. He couldn't get cross with Zeke, but he knew it was different when you read a thing yourself. Why, after that, what you read became a part of you! Anyhow, it was hard to keep awake in church. He knew Zeke was often sleepy there, just as he was, so his smile broadened as he stuffed the handkerchief into his pocket and rose, his arm linked in Ezekiel's.

"Let's help the ladies," Ezekiel suggested.

While they were setting plates on the table, the door opened again and Ebenezer Webster came in with another son. They brought more cold, snowy blasts with them, as they shook the melting snow onto the newly scrubbed pine floor.

Daniel's father was a handsome man with large features and a Roman nose. His eyes were dark and piercing, overhung by heavy brows; his hair was still coal black. He was tall, with broad shoulders, and carried himself more like a soldier than a farmer.

Like many of his neighbors, Ebenezer Webster, as a young man, had fought against the French and the Indians. The very farm on which he was now situated had been the scene of an Indian massacre. Near it had stood one of the last forts that protected the settlers against the redskins.

Later, Ebenezer Webster fought with the famous Rogers Rangers; and leading some seventy men, he pushed through the wilderness to the relief of Fort Ticonderoga. Still later he had served as a captain under General George Washington.

He had proved to be a leader of men in peace as well as in war, and only the year before he'd been placed on the bench of the Court of Common Pleas for his county.

Never having attended school, he had taught himself to read and write. So he was anxious to have his children go to school when possible, and was especially anxious to have little Daniel go. He even did an unusual thing: when the school was too far away for the boy to walk back and forth daily, he boarded Daniel in a home near the school so that the boy might have the extra months of instruction, while his older and stronger brothers worked on the farm.

At school Daniel had astonished not only his schoolmates but even his teacher, Mr. James Tappan, when in a contest to see how many verses from the Bible each child could repeat, Daniel won. He'd won by an ample margin, having gone on and on through sixty or seventy verses until Mr. Tappan had to stop him! Even then Daniel had offered to repeat several chapters more if anyone cared to listen.

When the family was seated around the supper table, Ebenezer Webster in a solemn voice asked the blessing, and as soon as he had finished, a clattering of knives and forks and spoons mingled with the loud voices.

While the others were busy eating and talking, Daniel drew the cotton handkerchief from his pocket again. He knew the first lines by heart, but wanted to learn the rest.

". . . secure the Blessings of Liberty to ourselves and our Posterity . . ." he muttered over and over, until his mother noticed he was not eating.

"Daniel, what are you doing? Why are you not eating your food?"

Zeke, who sat at his side, poked him gently and began to half feed him. When Daniel was reading, Zeke knew it was almost impossible to attract his attention to anything else, even food.

Now Mr. Webster turned to his youngest son. "I was talking to your schoolmaster the other day, Daniel, and he told me you were a great reader and that you won the prize for repeating all those Bible verses. I was satisfied." He drummed his fingers on the table for a moment, his dark eyes thoughtfully watching his young son. "But what do you suppose he said next? He said you'd never learn to write nicely, that your fingers were destined for the plow-tail!"

Before Daniel could reply, his brother Joe broke into a loud guffaw: "I'm afraid Master Tappan made a big mistake there. Why, little Daniel is the first Webster in ten generations who'll never even be able to hang a scythe!"

"He can plow, though," spoke up Zeke, as he pressed Daniel's arm affectionately. "He can plow as good as me!"

"There, boys, this is not a family contest, you know," said Mr. Webster kindly. "I didn't mean any harm, Daniel. I just thought you might try harder to write like General Washington and our great men. I'm right proud of you, Daniel, you know that." He rose from the table, and the rest of the family with him.

Daniel and Zeke begged their father to tell of his war experiences.

"Tell about the fighting at Bennington," urged Zeke, "where you were the first to scale the Tory breast-work, so covered with dust and powder when the battle was over that no one could see your face!"

"Tell about when you guarded President George Washington's tent at Dorchester Heights and he asked you all those questions," Daniel pleaded.

"You've heard all those tales dozens of times, boys," replied their father, as he relighted his pipe.

"But tell us again!" Daniel looked expectantly into his father's face.

"Tell about the traitor, Benedict Arnold," Zeke suggested.

"Yes, do, Father, do!" entreated Daniel. "That's best of all!"

Ebenezer Webster drew his chair back from the heat of the fire and crossed his long legs.

"Very well . . ." he took another puff on his pipe. "As you boys know, that happened at West Point up on the Hudson River in York state. It was after sundown when the news of Arnold's betrayal reached General Washington. He couldn't believe it at first. Benedict Arnold had been his friend. It's a hard thing, a very hard thing to have a friend betray the cause you thought you were both fighting for."

Ebenezer Webster paused to look first at Daniel, then Ezekiel, to see that his words sank in.

"There's nothing worse, I allow, than such betrayal. From a man with Benedict Arnold's advantages it would seem well nigh impossible. But there it was. The General had to admit it. It was then he called me in and I never felt sorrier for any human being than I did for General Washington that dreadful night . . ." He paused again.

"Go on! Go on!" urged Daniel and Zeke together.

"I was mighty proud when he called me in—me, a mere farmer—and said: 'I believe I can trust *you*.' Then he smiled sort of sadly, but kindly at me."

His story was followed by a long and thoughtful silence. Ebenezer Webster's children were very proud of their father.

Later that night, around midnight, Zeke and Daniel

lay in bed, talking. They discussed the verses in the yearly *Almanac,* which had recently arrived in the mail. Daniel started quoting a verse from the *Almanac,* but Zeke interrupted him:

"You've got the first two lines right, Daniel, but you're wrong about the third," Zeke insisted. Then he quoted the same verse.

"It's you who is wrong," Daniel retorted in a loud whisper.

He hopped out of bed. He knew they'd never agree, so proof was needed. The *Almanac* must be found and reread.

Daniel groped his way to the kitchen, where he lighted a candle. He then crept softly to the room where his bed-ridden grandmother was sleeping. His search was rewarded. He returned to his own room with the *Almanac* triumphantly clasped in his hand.

"Now I'll prove to you I'm right," he told Zeke, as he set the candle on the table and jumped into bed again.

Zeke grabbed the pamphlet from his hand and thumbed through the pages until he found the verse.

"No, you're not! I am! Here, read it yourself, Daniel."

The satisfaction Zeke felt overwhelmed his younger brother. Daniel said not a word but blew out the candle, turned over, and pretended to go to sleep.

Zeke, in bed beside him, was soon breathing deeply, and Daniel knew his brother was asleep. But he couldn't sleep. He tossed restlessly from side to side.

Finally, about two o'clock, Daniel was just drifting off when he saw a light in the passageway. It looked as if it came from his grandmother's room.

Bewildered, Daniel sprang from bed and rushed to open her door.

The room was on fire!

He suddenly realized that he himself must have

touched the candle to something in the room when he was hunting for the *Almanac*!

Daniel shrieked, "Fire! Fire!"

Soon his parents and brothers and sisters came running. Ebenezer Webster at once took charge. He ordered two of the boys to carry their grandmother to another room. Some of the family seized all the objects which were on fire and wrapped them in blankets, while others hurried for water. Finally, with everyone helping, the fire was put out, and they all went wearily back to their rooms.

After Daniel crawled back into bed, he shivered at the horror of what his carelessness might have caused. Then, his nostrils filled with the acrid odor of smoke, he fell asleep from sheer exhaustion and relief.

CHAPTER TWO

"LEARN, LEARN"

I WISH, DANIEL, YOU WOULDN'T SEE SO MUCH OF OLD man Wise, who tells you those stories about fighting with Admiral Byng. He's not the sort of companion I want you to have." His mother looked at her youngest son with concern.

"I only go there to read the newspaper to him," Daniel explained.

"Now, Daniel, don't prevaricate. You go to hear all those sailor tales he tells. I don't want your young head filled with such doings."

Daniel made no reply. It was his morning to work the sawmill for his father. He had been gathering together a couple of books to read while he worked. With Dr. Watts' *Psalms and Hymns* under his arm, and a paper copy of Pope's "Essay on Man" carefully held in his hand, he started off across the meadow to the banks of the Merrimac. His father had brought him the pamphlet of Pope's poetry and Daniel couldn't bear to let

11

it out of his sight. A new poem seemed a most wonderful possession.

At the mill he laid his books carefully on a little ledge, set the log and hoisted the gates. Then he opened Pope's "Essay on Man." Likely he could read it from cover to cover, he thought with satisfaction, in the twenty minutes or so it would take the saw to go through the tree trunk.

Daniel's absorption was so complete that he began reading aloud, scarcely aware of what he was doing:

" 'Laugh where we must, be candid where we can,
But vindicate the ways of God to Man.' "

Daniel's excitement was intense. He followed the words with the same animated interest that his brothers followed the spring planting.

A few weeks after this, on a hot July day, young Daniel was helping his father make hay. In the middle of the afternoon, they paused to rest under an elm tree. Daniel was tired from the exercise and the heat, but he tried not to show it. He was proud, indeed, when he felt he was a real help to his father on the farm.

As they rested, Mr. Webster talked about his friend, the Hon. Mr. Foster who lived over in Canterbury.

"My son, Foster is a worthy man—a member of Congress. If I had had his early education, I might have been in Philadelphia in his place." Ebenezer Webster sighed. "I came near to going to our national capital, as it was. But I missed it and must now work here . . ."

Daniel could not restrain himself. "Father," he said, placing his hand on Mr. Webster's arm, "Brother and I will work for you, and wear our hands out. But you shall rest." The tired, impressionable boy was now in tears.

"My child," said Ebenezer Webster gently, "it is of no importance to me, now. I could not give your older brothers the advantages of knowledge, but I can do something for you."

He paused and looked down at his young son.

"Exert yourself, improve your opportunities, learn, learn," he urged. "Then you won't need to go through the hardships which I have undergone and which have made me an old man before my time."

Daniel now redoubled his reading whenever he had the chance. *The Spectator*, a journal published in England, became his special delight. He read Joseph Addison's criticism of the ancient ballad, "Chevy Chase," solely for the sake of reading the connected song! It puzzled him that Addison should go to such trouble to prove that "Chevy Chase" was a good story, when it was so apparent to him that it was a grand one. It was young Daniel's introduction into the art of literary criticism, an art whose need he found it difficult to understand.

Whenever it rained or whenever Zeke could be spared from the heavier farm work, they would read together and then talk about what they read. Little Sally would sometimes try to join in, but without success. She even tagged along on their frequent fishing trips. But it was only at berrying time that her brothers found her really useful. Then their sister's fingers could pick a pailful of juicy fruit before the boys were well started.

That winter Daniel was in better health than usual. When spring came he was astonished to learn he was to go to a private school some distance from home!

One May morning his father brought two horses to

the front of the house. He helped Daniel onto the one with the side-saddle, piling innumerable bundles round about him. It embarrassed the young boy to ride in a lady's saddle, but he resolved to make the best of it.

It took father and son two days and nights to reach the famous preparatory school which John Phillips had founded at Exeter. Dr. Benjamin Abbot was then, and for forty years thereafter, Head of the Academy; but when the Websters arrived he was ill. The Reverend Joseph Stevens Buckminster received them.

As the Reverend Buckminster observed Daniel coldly, the boy was for the first time conscious of his homespun clothes and home-made boots. His rustic appearance was, he recalled, in marked contrast to that of the young boys he'd seen about the grounds as he rode past.

"Young man," said Reverend Buckminster, "what is your age?"

"Fourteen," replied Daniel, hardly able to command the tones of his voice.

"Take this Bible, Master Webster, and read this chapter to me." He indicated a chapter as he handed the book to the boy.

The passage was the one in the Gospel of St. Luke which describes the conspiracy of Judas with the chief priests and scribes, the Last Supper and Judas' betrayal of Christ, the three denials of Peter, and the scene in the house of the high priest.

Daniel knew it almost by heart. In his young imagination he had often relived the awful and fatal days. Softly at first, then clearly and easily as the familiar words restored his confidence, he read the passages with appreciation and feeling. His fervor astonished the young minister.

When Daniel finished and looked up, the Reverend Buckminster was looking at him with a kind but quizzical expression.

"Young man," he said, "you are qualified to enter this institution."

The nine months Daniel spent at Exeter were the most difficult ones he had yet experienced. The other lads were amused at his rural appearance and made fun of him. He was so shy that he could not find his voice to recite before the school. Many a piece he committed to memory in his room, where he would rehearse it over and over; but when he was confronted with his smiling fellow pupils and the over-sober Masters, he could not even raise himself from his chair. Their eyes, all intent upon him, paralyzed him.

Yet when it was time to leave, the young minister who had received him assured the fifteen-year-old boy that if he would return the next term he would be put in a far higher class. Nor would he be hindered another year by association with boys who cared more for dress and play than for solid accomplishment.

Young Daniel was overcome by the unexpected praise. In his heart he resolved to return.

But this could not be. His father was a very poor man. He simply had no more money to spend on Daniel's education.

So, with a heavy heart, but determined to make the best of what he had, young Daniel began to teach little boys in his uncle's school in Salisbury.

Ebenezer Webster was not happy about this. He often talked it over with his wife and older children. But there simply was no money to be used for the further education of his youngest son.

Luckily for Daniel, there lived in his home town the

Reverend Wood, who spent his spare time educating boys to enter the University. Reverend Wood was a friend of Dr. Abbot, Headmaster of the Phillips Academy in Exeter. These kindly men talked together about Daniel, and then Reverend Wood called on Ebenezer Webster.

Consequently, a few days later Mr. Webster told Daniel that he'd decided to let the Reverend Wood prepare him for college, and that the money would somehow be found for tuition.

"For college?" The young boy was obviously overwhelmed.

"Yes, Daniel. The Reverend Wood says he can prepare you for Dartmouth."

"But, Father, where will the money come from? How can it be spared for me?" Daniel was overcome.

"Why, Daniel, you know that I live only for my children," his father replied. "If you do all you can for me, I will do all I can for you."

Daniel was deeply moved. He could only press his father's hands. Then he burst into tears of joy.

The Reverend Wood set the lad to studying Virgil and Tully, and soon Daniel found he enjoyed these Latin writers. Reading Latin was no longer a dreaded task but a delight. He spent hours denouncing Cataline with great vehemence.

In those days, college preparation was mostly a matter of learning Latin and Greek. Never had the Reverend Wood had a more earnest or determined student. By the following July he knew that the boy was ready. So before he was sixteen years old, Daniel Webster set out for the New Hampshire college.

DARTMOUTH

THE APPOINTED DAY CAME, THE DAY IN AUGUST when Daniel started for Dartmouth. He mounted his horse, which was loaded with the possessions he must take with him—his bedding, his clothes (what few there were!) his books, and a parcel of food to see him through the journey.

He had said good-by to his father and brothers who had to go to work in the fields, and to his mother, whom he had left in the kitchen with a tearful Sally.

Only Zeke, straight and tall, stood there with a hand on the horse's mane, smiling into the face of his brother whose hands grasped the reins.

"Look cheerful, Dan'l," he said. "You're off, maybe, to a hard life, but a good one. You're going to get some learning. There's a future before you. Maybe you'll be a great man. Anyhow, great or not, you'll be the better man for it. I count on you."

"That's what troubles me, Zeke. Here I'm getting the

17

chance you ought to have. I don't know, but I feel you'd make a better scholar and a better man than I would. It makes me feel bad that you can't go in my place, or with me." Daniel looked affectionately at his brother, whose smile widened.

"So that's what's troubling you, Dan'l! Put it right out of your mind, do you hear? Look at the man our father is! Did he ever go to school? No, he didn't! He's self-educated. Yet there is not a finer man in this county or any other, is there?"

Daniel nodded his head, while Ezekiel went on:

"It's what a man is that counts. It's what he's done with his chances. It's what he's done with his life. It's what he's gotten out of it—yes, even if the chances were against him."

"I think so, too, Zeke. Yet . . ."

"Daniel," Ezekiel brusquely interrupted him, "you were going to say, 'why should I have the chance to go to college and not you?' Who knows, I may go, too, some day."

Daniel's eyes brightened. "That would be wonderful, Zeke! May it come true soon!"

"Well, you'd better get going, if you ever expect to be in Hanover." Ezekiel laughed and slapped the horse on the thigh. "Good-by, Dan. And a lot of luck. Write soon how you're getting along."

"All right, Zeke, good-by!" Daniel made a chirping sound with his mouth, shook the reins, and the horse started. Presently Daniel looked back and waved. Then the horse took a turn in the road and was soon lost to sight behind the trees.

Daniel went on thinking of his brother. He was already beginning to be homesick for Zeke!

His road lay along the banks of the Merrimac. The morning was clear and bright, crisp and not too warm,

in spite of it being August. Suddenly he put the sadness of parting behind him. His eyes sought the long, broken range of mountains, which terminated in the Kearsarge. Affectionately Daniel patted his horse's neck.

He was thinking of a book he had recently read, one he had borrowed from the newly formed Boscawen library. It was the story of Don Quixote, by a Spanish writer named Cervantes. Never had he read a book with greater zest. He had read on and on, so fascinated he couldn't lay it down until the last page. Don Quixote riding his horse, Rosinante, strongly appealed to young Daniel. Here was a man, ridiculous though he was, who had set out on a journey to do chivalrous deeds, to fight wrong wherever he found it. Perhaps he could emulate Quixote some day, when he had been educated and gone out into the world. Not that he looked forward to this going out into the world. He more than half envied Zeke, and loved the farm as much as his brother did. Why was it he could never hang a scythe, why had he no skill with his hands like all his brothers?

Swaying to the easy movement of the horse, young Daniel resolved things in his mind. He was going to Dartmouth, but he would have to work hard to achieve a goal.

As he rode along the banks of the Merrimac, he soon arrived at the confluence of two rivers: The Pemigewasset, which rises in the White Mountains, and the Winnepiscogee, which issues from the lake of the same name; both join with the Merrimac.

Daniel jumped down from his horse, tied him to a tree, and took from the saddlebag a small compressed bundle of hay, which he offered to the beast.

For a few moments he gazed at the rivers, in one of which the water ran cold and in the other warm. He thought of a strange fact his father had told him: when the Merrimac was full of fish, the salmon and the shad parted company at the meeting of the two smaller rivers. The shad went into the lakes, while the salmon went on up the mountain current, both continuing their ascent to their destination.

He wondered why. There was a reason for everything, he thought. Fish must be just like men, each kind of fish clung to its own kind, just as he, Daniel, preferred his own family to any other family.

And again, as he sat down and ate his cold lunch, he thought of his father, of Ezekiel, of little Sally. He must be worthy of them; he must live up to their expectations of him.

A couple of days later Daniel reached Hanover. He stabled his horse near the common and looked around. Never had he seen so many young men walking about. They seemed to be everywhere, going and coming in twos and threes. The big building on the hill, he thought, must be the college. He was wondering whether he should go directly there or look about first for a boardinghouse, when he saw a young man approaching.

"Are you a new student?" asked the stranger. "My name is George Farrar. Can I help you?"

"I have come from the Reverend Samuel Wood of Boscawen, who thinks I am prepared to be a freshman at the college," Daniel replied shyly.

"I think my father knows Reverend Wood," said young Farrar. "He has prepared many students for entrance to Dartmouth. Would you like to go with me to our home? We always have some boys boarding with us."

Thus, fortunately, did the college years start out

among friends. Daniel's freshman year passed rapidly as he spent endless hours reading and studying.

On a warm July day of the following summer he was walking across the now-familiar common when someone took hold of his arm.

"Why, Hervey Bingham, where did you come from?" Daniel greeted the handsomely clad, bright-eyed boy.

"I'm now a freshman," James Hervey Bingham informed him. "Do you know, Daniel, I've been hearing tales about you ever since you left us in Exeter."

Daniel grinned. He had liked this gay, rich youngster in those early days at Phillips Academy.

"I've not only learned that you're the best all-around student here," young Bingham continued, "but that you hold the United Fraternity spellbound with the flow of your golden words!"

"How can you believe such nonsense?" Daniel's deep-set eyes twinkled. "You, if anyone, should know how hard it is for me to find my tongue in the presence of fellow students."

"Oh, Brother Daniel," crowed Bingham with amusement, "don't try to pull wool over my eyes! You're no longer the same frightened lad I knew at Exeter. I could see that clear across this common!"

"It's only my retentive memory that's given me what little reputation I have here . . ."

"Why, Daniel, what a modest violet you pretend to be," laughed young Bingham. "Why, I've heard that you rise up before an audience with the aplomb of David Garrick himself, and peer with your black eyes out from under those over-hanging brows of yours, while in solemn tones you recite poetry—your own compositions, I've heard tell, and with every line ending in i-o-n!

"Now don't deny it," he interrupted Daniel's effort to reply. "I have it on the best authority."

From the happy day of this meeting with an old friend, fishing parties and gunning expeditions occasionally lent diversion to student activities. On these expeditions Daniel would take along a volume of poetry. He claimed he mesmerized the fish by reading aloud! However much truth or fiction there was in his banter, he did usually return with the largest catch.

So in work and in play time passed to the May vacation of his sophomore year, when he visited his family in Salisbury.

He and Zeke still shared the same big bed, and that first night they talked until dawn. Ezekiel Webster was now a strongly built, robust youth of nineteen.

"I've thought of going West, Daniel, and trying to strike out for myself," Zeke said.

But Daniel soon convinced him that they should both stay near their aging parents.

"What I think you should do, Zeke, is to go to Reverend Wood, as I did, and join me later at Dartmouth. Now don't say another word. Being older, you should have had the first chance, but it's never too late to mend," observed Daniel. "I'll see Father about it right after breakfast, and you must back me up."

After their scheme was told to their father the next morning, he looked at his son home from college, then at his right-hand helper on the farm.

"You know, both of you, I only live for my children," Mr. Webster said. "But I have to consider your mother and two unmarried sisters . . ."

"They'll want Zeke to have his chance," Daniel insisted. "I can stop college and work awhile if need be. I'll help out all I can."

"But, boys, it will take every cent I'm worth. I'll

have to put a second mortgage on the farm. I'd take that risk gladly, but it's the women folk I'm concerned about."

"You've admitted it isn't fair for me to be given all the advantages of an education when Zeke has nothing to look forward to," Daniel said.

"You take up the matter with your mother and sisters and I'll abide by what they say," said their father. "My friends and neighbors will think I've taken leave of my senses if I send a great, strapping farmer lad of twenty to prepare for study in college when I need his help on the farm," he chuckled.

"You're an independent man, Father," Daniel's voice was filled with pride. "You've the moral courage to do what you think should be done, even if our friends and neighbors believe no able-bodied man should go to college."

"My health's far from good, you know. We four could later be a great burden to you two boys," the older man cautioned the youths.

Daniel promised his mother and sisters to assume his father's protective place, and when he returned to Hanover he knew Zeke would join him there later. At Reverend Wood's, Zeke proved to be a genius at Latin and an excellent student in all his studies.

To help Zeke out financially at Reverend Wood's, Daniel worked for a weekly newspaper in Hanover. The small salary he received for making literary excerpts for its columns and writing an occasional piece of his own, paid his board in college.

CHAPTER FOUR

DANIEL HELPS HIS BROTHER

IN HIS JUNIOR YEAR AT DARTMOUTH, DANIEL WAS ONE of twelve in his class to achieve Phi Beta Kappa. Another honor came to the eighteen-year-old country lad. The people of Hanover chose him to give the Fourth of July oration. How hard he worked on this first public speech, how often he read it over to his patient friends, how histrionically he practiced it before his friend Bingham! Bingham heard the speech so often, he almost memorized it himself!

"In the adoption of our present systems of jurisprudence, we see the powers necessary for government voluntarily flowing from the people, their only origin, and directed to the public good, their only proper object . . ." young Bingham thought very fine.

When on July Fourth Daniel Webster came to speak before his first large audience in the Hanover meeting hall, he asked: "But why shall every quarrel on the other side of the Atlantic interest us in its issue? Why shall the rise or depression of every party there produce here a corresponding vibration? Was this continent designed as a mere satellite to the other?"

It was obvious that his listeners were in full agreement with the answer almost before he gave it to them in his solemn tones:

"The natural superiority of America clearly indicates that it was designed to be inhabited by a nobler race of men, possessing a superior form of government, superior patriotism, superior talents, and superior virtues.

"Let then the nations of the East muster their strength in destroying each other. Let them aspire to conquest and contend for dominion till their continent is deluged in blood. But let none, however elated by victory, however proud of triumph, ever presume to intrude on the neutral position assumed by our country!"

Scarcely were the last words uttered when deafening applause greeted the young orator. Although he was still somewhat shy, Daniel received their plaudits as naturally as if this were a daily occurrence.

How he wished Zeke could have heard him and seen the enthusiasm he aroused! His first triumph was not half as sweet as it would have been with his brother at his side. Daniel had to content himself with the knowledge that the fee he received for his oration would help with his brother's expenses at Reverend Wood's.

The next summer Zeke joined him at Dartmouth. By then Daniel had a large tutoring business going well. He received a small steady income from that and for his work as "Icarus" on the little weekly newspaper.

Zeke heard Daniel's solemn oration on the death of his friend Simonds and, when graduation days were at hand, his more colorful oration before the United Fraternity.

Zeke was annoyed that his brother had not been chosen by the college as the Valedictory speaker. How could Dr. Shurtleff and President Wheeler think Caleb Tenny was a better speaker than his young brother? Surely Daniel had the best all-around record of achievement in his class as a genius for public speaking! Zeke was distressed and puzzled, but since Daniel said nothing about the matter, Zeke did not speak of it to him. Watching Daniel's smiling face, when he received his diploma with the other members of his class, Zeke decided the accomplishment of being a college graduate was enough for Daniel. Zeke knew it would be enough for himself, too, if he ever managed to achieve it.

When the boys went home for the vacation, old Ebenezer approached Daniel about his future plans.

"Teaching isn't as good as law," he repeated stubbornly when Daniel spoke of helping out with the school.

"But, Father, it will be years before I can earn any money in law. What will Zeke do? How can he go on to Dartmouth?"

"You go across the street to Mr. Thompson's office and read law, Daniel, and I'll do what I can for Zeke," his father insisted. "There's a future in law for a man who can speak in public as Zeke says you can."

So Daniel spent a few months reading Sir Edward Coke's famous cases and Sir William Blackstone's *Commentaries on the Laws of England,* in the office which he had often swept out as a boy of thirteen. But soon the urgent need of money took Daniel to Fryeburg, Maine, to teach school.

He traveled the miles of snow and cold on horseback, with his wardrobe and books in his saddlebags; and then he sold the animal when he arrived at his destination. He boarded with the Register of Deeds and spent his evenings copying these deeds, thereby earning enough for his board. This austere life continued until he received his first-term payment from the school.

No sooner was the money in his hands than he hastened to Dartmouth to give it to Zeke. Again, when the next term was over, all his money went to help his brother.

Even so, both boys together could not earn enough to keep Zeke, who had become as brilliant as his younger brother in his college work, at Dartmouth.

During the years that young Daniel studied the difficult law books at Mr. Thompson's, he and Zeke were often penniless. Daniel sold everything he had, but still he could not raise enough money for himself and his brother. Neither of the boys could have existed as students during those years had not their father given them all he earned from his County Court judgeship.

Finally Zeke gave up the losing fight and decided he must quit school and work. Through Daniel he obtained a position in a Boston school, where he could teach during the day and have his nights for study.

Yet these years were not all struggle and work. At times Daniel's irrepressible spirit would break forth, as when he wrote:

> Come then, tobacco, new-found friend,
> Come and thy suppliant attend
>   In each dull lonely hour;

    And though misfortunes lie around,
  Thicker than hailstones on the ground,
     I'll rest upon thy power . . .

It didn't make it any less difficult for young Daniel to know that one of his friends was in easy circumstances and living well, or that another friend was well situated and "caught in the lure of an heiress as a pheasant in a snare," as his constant correspondence informed him.

Daniel spent an occasional evening with Sally and her friends. He went to church every Sunday as he had all his life. But as quiet day followed quiet day, and weeks stretched into months, he realized more and more that this life was not congenial to his convivial spirits. He chafed continually.

Although he enjoyed fishing and hunting and often took long canters on his horse, these solitary diversions did little to revive his spirits. Often the months seemed endless as he sat up late over his books in the flickering candlelight.

He found himself inclined to agree with Mr. Bennet, who said that a lawyer who preserves his integrity unspotted deserves a place in the calendar of saints!

Ezekiel Webster had made an admirable record at Dartmouth, and the faculty did an unusual thing when it permitted him to teach in Boston for half of his senior year, yet return and receive the coveted diploma with his class. At this time Zeke, who had reached his middle twenties, was nearly six feet in height, finely proportioned, with a commanding presence for so young a man. His cheerful, friendly face made him instantly popular; he was exceedingly courteous to everyone. From the day he came to their school to teach, young Dr. and Mrs. Perkins were both delighted with him.

When Daniel arrived to take his brother's place at the Boston school so that Zeke could return to Dartmouth and graduate, the four sat in the garden and talked late on Ezekiel's final evening there.

"You look as confident and sanguine as ever, Mr. Daniel," young Mrs. Perkins smiled at the dark, slender figure seated at her side.

"And why shouldn't I be? Is not this admirable brother of mine about to receive his degree at Dartmouth where he has been asked to give the English Oration?"

"Are you always made happy by the success of others?" The young woman studied Daniel Webster with great curiosity. "I haven't observed this to be a trait of young men."

"Daniel and I aren't just brothers, you know," Ezekiel said. "As Horace, the Roman poet, said in his Epistles:

'Fraternis animis quidquid negat alter et alter,
Annuimus pariter vetuli notique columbi.'"

(With brotherly spirits we old familiar doves agree with each other equally, and whatever one denies the other also denies.)

The laughter which followed was interrupted by Dr. Perkins who asked, "And do you agree with your brother, Daniel, that with the election of Mr. Gilman as Governor of our state of New Hampshire, democracy has triumphed just as it has in Washington with the election of the atheist, Thomas Jefferson?"

"These are serious times for all people," replied Daniel. "I was shocked when Nat Gilman received more votes for Treasurer of New Hampshire than there were voters in order to win! Such trickery in a brother of the Governor will soil the fair name of our state."

"In my opinion there is not a nook or corner that will not be revolutionized," observed Zeke in a somber voice. "The contagion of democracy will pervade every place and corrupt every generous and manly sentiment. It cannot be successfully resisted. The pestilence will spread in a favorable state of the atmosphere, notwithstanding all the medical exertions of the most skillful physicians."

"Yes," agreed Daniel. "We must make still more effort to gain a Federalist majority, not only in New Hampshire, but in the whole country."

"How serious you men are!" laughed young Mrs. Perkins. "Let me get you a cool drink. I guarantee it will dispel the gloom, even such gloom as the election of Gilman has cast over all Federalists."

"Gilman is of little account," Dr. Perkins said. "It is Thomas Jefferson who will ruin our fair land; that is, he will if he can!" He paused to relight his pipe. "Luckily, since he became President four years ago, he has not been able to fulfill the dangerous promises he made. We Federalists have seen to that!"

"But since his re-election," interposed Ezekiel, "I fear the worst!"

"Thomas Jefferson could hardly better Alexander Hamilton's basic financial policies," observed Daniel. "And he hasn't been able to break our hold on the Judiciary, the gods be praised!"

As soon as Daniel and Zeke were alone that night Daniel exclaimed, "I came within an ace of being appointed clerk of the Court of Common Pleas for Hillsborough county!"

"Within an ace, Daniel," laughed Ezekiel. "If that's

all, you're no better off than if you hadn't come within an ace!"

"Just the same, I mean never to distrust the gods again," asserted Daniel.

"Perhaps you can get it later. It would be a very good thing and I advise you to use all honest means to procure it," said Zeke, seriously. "Any office where you can earn money and at the same time learn the legal forms, will give you many advantages which you don't have at present."

"Oh, I mean to read the law in the finest office in Boston," Daniel retorted grandly.

"But you haven't a single letter of introduction, Daniel," his brother warned. "Nor do you know a soul here in Boston but Dr. Perkins and me. How do you propose to manage such a feat?"

"I don't propose to manage it, dear Zeke," laughed Daniel. "I leave it to the gods that be. I shall trust them!"

"SOMETHING OR NOTHING"

EXPECTING EZEKIEL BACK FROM NEW HAMPSHIRE, Daniel decided that he must do something drastic to help the gods along. Up to this time his efforts to find an office in which he could read the law had been fruitless. He began to wonder if it would not be better for him to return to Boscawen and get a copy of his college degree and a letter from Mr. Thompson; each office he had entered had asked for these.

His self-confidence had not lessened, but he was becoming more and more aware of the difficulty of finding a good law clerkship in Boston, where he was unknown. Dr. Perkins had done everything within his power, but so far this had led to nothing.

It was a hot, sultry morning, and as Daniel walked along Short Street he saw a familiar figure approaching.

"Why, Mr. Bradley!" he exclaimed, as he recognized

an acquaintance from Fryeburg, Maine. "What has brought you here?"

"I might ask the same of you, Mr. Webster!"

"I'm looking for a berth in a law office," Daniel readily explained.

"So you've given up teaching school? We've missed you and often hoped you would return to Fryeburg."

The young men were walking toward the Scollay's building, and when they reached it Daniel paused.

"A lawyer, in whose office I'd rather be than any other in Boston, has rooms here." Daniel looked longingly up at the door. "But I don't know Mr. Gore and I have no one to introduce me to him."

"It wouldn't be the Honorable Christopher Gore who has just returned from eight years in London, as a Commissioner under the British Treaty, would it?"

"How did you guess? Do you know him?" asked Daniel.

"Not to say know him, but I know of him," replied his acquaintance. "Let's go in and introduce each other to him. Then we'll both know him. This is a free country, Daniel," he went on when he saw that Daniel looked dubious. "Nothing ventured, nothing won, you know."

Into the offices of Christopher Gore went the two irrepressible young men. Mr. Bradley murmured something by way of introduction. Daniel couldn't find his tongue. He stood quietly aside and solemnly surveyed the fine office with its rows of books to the ceiling, and the portly white-haired man who was, in turn, surveying him.

Impressed by the slender youth with his intense black eyes and serious expression, Christopher Gore tried to relieve Daniel's embarrassment.

"Tell me about yourself, young man," he courteously suggested.

"I heard you needed a clerk. I want so much to study with you that I have come in here this way. I must apologize. You would not care to have me after this, I fear."

Christopher Gore laughed. "I certainly don't wish to fill my office with clerks, but I have considered taking on one or two. How did you hear about it, young man?"

"I think it was through some friends of my father or brother," Daniel answered. "Mr. Peabody knows me and I think you know him. I have been reading law in Boscawen with Mr. Thompson until now."

Mr. Peabody had been Mr. Gore's classmate. He decided to give this quiet young man a trial. "My young friend, you look as if you might be trusted," Christopher Gore said. "You have told me you came to Boston to study, not to waste time. I will take you at your word. You may hang up your hat at once; go into the other room; take your book and sit down to read it. At your convenience you can write to New Hampshire for your letters and credentials."

It was a full week before the Honorable Christopher Gore knew the name of his new clerk, but before that he knew he had made no mistake in taking him. He recognized Daniel's ability and knew he was a young man of exceptional talents.

The twentieth of July remained long in Daniel Webster's memory. The gods had certainly smiled on him!

For the next nine months he read diligently. He studied not only books but men. From August he attended sessions of the Supreme Court and reported all their decisions; he also attended the Circuit Court of the United States.

When he had been in Mr. Gore's office about six months, he received the appointment as clerk of the Hillsborough Court of Common Pleas. Ezekiel again urged him to accept it.

Daniel was immensely elated. It seemed to him equivalent to a presidential election. He could scarcely contain himself.

The income from the work would be fifteen hundred a year, and this sum was sorely needed by Daniel and his family. At last he had the chance to make good his promises to his father!

The young man could not contain his excitement. He rushed into the office of Christopher Gore, waving his father's letter that contained the wonderful news.

"Sit down, Daniel," said Christopher Gore kindly. "This is surely an honor for a young man and one you richly deserve."

Daniel beamed as he sat down eagerly before Mr. Gore's desk.

"Yes, it was very civil of their Honors of the Bench," the Honorable Christopher Gore continued judiciously, "very civil. They intend it for a mark of confidence in you and for a mark of respect to your father. You must acknowledge it civilly."

Daniel's face fell. "Acknowledge it civilly?" he answered in disbelief.

"You look dismayed!" exclaimed Mr. Gore. "Surely you didn't intend to give up your study now that you are within reach of the bar? There is no reason you should not make your way in the law. You have an admirable mind for it. This clerkship, as you know, depends on the will of others. You will never be your own master if you accept it. Those that give you the position now can as easily take it away."

"But my father urges it. My brother, Ezekiel, urged

me to accept it if it was offered to me," stammered Daniel.

Mr. Gore had never looked more fatherly. "My dear young man, you must take my advice. I don't like to set up my opinion against that of your family. But I am sure you will never regret it if you decline, and equally sure you will eternally regret it if you accept. So I mean to do all in my power to keep you with me until you are admitted to the bar."

Daniel shook his head. He was still uncertain. What would his father say? What would Zeke think of it? How could he explain to Mr. Gore their great need of money?

"Go on," Mr. Gore was saying, as if he could read his mind, "and finish your studies. You are poor enough, I know well, but there are far greater evils than poverty, young man."

Daniel still could find no answer. He was bewildered, but his heart was full of gratitude for this kind advice.

"Live on no man's favor," continued Christopher Gore kindly. "What bread you eat, let it be the bread of independence; pursue your profession, make yourself useful to your friends and a little formidable to your enemies, and you have nothing to fear from the future."

Daniel knew well that he must follow this sage advice. But how hard it would be to turn down the appointment, for the clerkship offered a nice income to the struggling young man.

The hardest part was yet to come, however, for he must win his father over to an agreement with his decision. He knew it would come as a thunderbolt to his aging parent, who had always hoped Daniel might receive the clerkship, and who was filled with pride when he wrote his son the great news.

Ebenezer Webster had been ill recently. His sons had moved away and he was a very lonely old man. Daniel knew his father wanted him to settle near home. He must not leave him under such a delusion an hour more than was necessary.

He at once looked around for a sleigh, as no stage-coaches ran to the interior of New Hampshire, and was lucky to find one in the marketplace. He set off at once and within three days had reached his father's house.

It was evening when he arrived and old Ebenezer Webster received him with evident joy. Daniel tried to put on an air of gaiety as well.

"My boy, my boy," his parent's eyes were filled with tears. "I knew you would come at once."

Daniel's heart was heavy. He wished he could die on the spot! But there was no help for it. He was on his own now.

"I shall write them a most courteous letter," he said slowly. "It was exceedingly civil of them to offer me the clerkship."

His father's puzzled expression tore at his heart.

"If I could consent to record anybody's judgments it would be those judges of whom you are one," Daniel rattled on, scarcely knowing what he was saying. "It would indeed be an honor . . ."

Ebenezer Webster's astonishment now turned to amazement. Surely his son did not expect to decline the munificent offer! He studied the flushed dark face so like his own. He did not know what to make of his youngest son.

"Do you intend to decline this offer?" he finally asked.

"Most certainly," replied Daniel promptly, anxious to get the worst over with as soon as possible. "I cannot think of doing otherwise. I should be very sorry if I could not do better in the near future than become a clerk, even for fifteen hundred dollars a year—not to speak of the more distant future. Such a clerkship has no future at all!"

The older man made no reply. He was watching his son, as if hypnotized.

"In the courts I mean to use my tongue, not my pen," Daniel went on eagerly. "I mean to be an actor, not a register of other men's actions. I hope yet, sir, to astonish you in your own Court with my professional attainments!"

Ebenezer Webster rocked violently in his chair. His eyes flashed. But when he at last turned to Daniel, his eyes held an expression of pride. Daniel knew he had won his father to some measure of agreement. His father was gratified that Daniel clung to an honorable profession with such ardor.

"Well, my son, your mother has always said you would come to something or nothing, she was not sure which; I think you are now about settling that doubt for her."

Daniel remained with his father another week. He gave him the three hundred dollars he had borrowed in Boston, to help his parent out of present financial difficulties. But no one in the family spoke of his decision during his stay. It was a closed subject from the moment he talked to his father on the night of his homecoming.

CHAPTER SIX

A NOVICE LAWYER

SIX MONTHS LATER, AFTER ZEKE HAD GRADUATED from Dartmouth and entered the study of law, the Webster brothers were seated in Daniel's new law office in Boscawen. He was now entirely on his own. How proud he had felt when he nailed the shingle in place on the doorpost!

In March, Mr. Gore had introduced Daniel to the judges of the Suffolk Court of Common Pleas. Mr. Gore, who spoke enthusiastically of Daniel Webster's diligence and ability, moved he be admitted to the bar. Mr. Gore did not hesitate to say that he was confident his pupil would far out-distance all competitors. This made Daniel very proud and he was determined not to disappoint his sponsor.

At first Daniel hoped to start his own law practice in Portsmouth, New Hampshire's largest and most important city. But when he heard that his father was ill and needed him, he gave up Portsmouth for Boscawen

41

in order to be near his parents. And now he had finally opened his office, and Zeke had come to visit.

Zeke turned away from the bookshelf, hesitated a moment, then blurted out: "You seemed very interested in the young lady who was with Judge and Mrs. Kelley, Daniel."

Daniel blushed and didn't reply at once.

"You aren't serious about her, surely," Zeke went on. "We're neither of us in a position to marry yet."

"How well I know that, Zeke!"

"Well, out with it! Who's this young lady who causes you to blush?"

"She's Mrs. Kelley's sister from up state, and she's visiting them. Her name is Grace Fletcher."

"Grace Fletcher," repeated Zeke, "Grace is an unusual name in these parts."

"It's a beautiful name, Zeke," said Daniel softly.

"Come, Daniel, tell me all about it!"

"There's nothing to tell. You saw her for yourself, so you know she's charming but not pretty; animated, yes, and of such sweet seriousness . . ."

"Why, Dan, you sound poetical!"

Again his young brother turned a deep crimson. "You should know her, Zeke! Not that I know her well as yet, although the Kelleys have often asked me there." Daniel paused. "She has such a winning personality. She is so unaffected and interested, not at all like the silly girls I've known in Hanover, or even in Boston. Her father was a clergyman."

"Was? Is he dead?"

"He died when Grace was only four years old, but her mother married another clergyman, the Reverend Christopher Paige, who's been a second father to her."

"Well, if she's kind to my brother I'll give her all the virtues," Zeke looked fondly at Daniel. "But don't get too involved," he cautioned. "It may be years before we can have our own families. Father is ailing, and so is Mother. We promised him . . ."

"I know, Zeke! Do you think I would have come to Boscawen for any reason but to be near him? My help with the farm may not amount to what yours would, Zeke, but such as it has been, Father needed it."

"If you had gone to Portsmouth you might never have met Mrs. Kelley's sister, so you see virtue is occasionally rewarded in this world!"

Zeke began to pace up and down the small office. "I'm working overtime with Blackstone and Coke," he observed, "but I don't think I can be admitted to the bar for a couple of years. You'll have to carry on here until then."

Zeke stopped and looked down at his slender brother. "Don't allow yourself to be depressed, Daniel. I know a life of writs and summonses is dull for you, but you're working yourself up not only in Hillsborough county but also in Rockingham and Grafton as well. You're learning more about human nature every day."

Ezekiel Webster was not admitted to the bar until two years later. When he was, he came to Boscawen to carry on Daniel's law practice there. In the meantime old Ebenezer Webster had died, but not until his youngest son had argued a case before him. The boys felt the loss of their father keenly, but they were now grown men with problems and lives of their own.

During his years in Boscawen, Daniel had done his best to look after his father's farm as well as build up his own law practice. He had been admitted as attorney and counselor to the Superior Court the previous May. But now that his father was no longer able to advise him, he was relieved when Zeke, who was an expert farmer, took over in his stead.

When their father died the boys had jointly undertaken the care and support of their mother and sisters. Daniel alone assumed the burden of his father's debts which weighed heavily on him for ten years.

Daniel's acquaintance with Grace Fletcher had slowly ripened into a close friendship. On the last night before he left for Portsmouth, he drove over to Salisbury to the home of Judge Isaac Kelley. Both Judge Kelley and his wife Rebecca were away for the evening, so Grace received him alone in the front parlor.

She had been reading an essay by Daniel in the *Monthly Anthology,* a Boston magazine, which she put down as she rose to greet him.

"It's odd to find you reading, Grace," Daniel teased. "Usually you're occupied with some utterly feminine task—knitting, embroidering a sampler, copying out a new recipe . . ."

"Did you really think I never read?" Grace countered. "Your essay is wonderful, simply wonderful! Why, you write almost as beautifully as you speak!"

They had seated themselves on the sofa and as Grace reached to the table again to take up the magazine, Daniel caught her hand.

"No, Grace, you can read that when I have gone. I want to look at you and talk with you during the few hours left to me."

A delicate flush played on the cheeks of the serious young woman, but she made no reply. Folding her hands in her lap, she looked adoringly at Daniel.

"Oh, Grace," Daniel half groaned. "I . . ."

"You were reading me Mr. Milton's poetry the last time you were here." Grace Fletcher finally broke the silence. "Do you remember?"

"I've thought about that since and how interested you were," Daniel replied glumly. "Would I were a great poet! Poets and painters seem to spring full-grown from their cradles. Musicians, too, are born, not made. But a lawyer must be made. Years of study are essential. It is an artificial calling, but a great one if it is practiced in the true spirit of the profession."

"Oh, yes, Daniel, one must always work and study to be truly great. I think Mr. Milton must have worked and studied, too, or how did he know the Bible and Greek and Latin mythological tales by heart?"

Daniel was silent.

Grace tried to relieve his apparent distress. "You're tired, Daniel," she said gently. "The death of your father and all the work on the farm—in addition to your practice—have worn you out."

"True, I'm not strong like Zeke. Would I were! I want to move mountains, Grace, do you know that?"

Grace smiled tenderly, as she watched him get up from the sofa and begin to stride up and down the parlor.

"I shall not swerve from the path of fame I have planned for myself. I shall not give my life up to petti-fogging. I mean to acquire more and more knowledge. I shall model myself on Cicero!" His voice rang out as he paced about the room.

Watching him, Grace felt certain that Daniel would one day be as famous as the Roman lawyer and orator.

"Oh, Grace, what will our country come to if this love of money remains the ruling passion? It has taken root deeply and I fear it will never be eradicated. While this holds everything in its grip, America will produce few great characters." He stood before her, scowling.

"My profession of the law is a fine profession, Grace,

only if practiced in the right spirit. It is a fraud and an iniquity when its true spirit is supplanted by a spirit of mischief-making and money-catching!"

Daniel had never talked like this before. Grace could see that something had moved him deeply. Perhaps he was more disturbed at giving up his Boscawen practice than he knew. Of course the farm had been left to his brother, so it was a sensible arrangement. But Grace had learned many lessons in her twenty-six years of life in New Hampshire, and one of these was that what seemed sensible and right was not always easy to do.

"We shall miss you, Daniel, when you are far away in Portsmouth," she said gently.

"Will you?" Daniel looked deeply into her eyes. "Oh, Grace, if only I can succeed there as I believe I shall!"

"But of course you will, Daniel. We all have the greatest confidence in your ability. Why, Isaac said . . ."

"I won't say that Judge Kelley's opinion is not valuable," Daniel interrupted her, "but it is *your* opinion, Grace, in which I am particularly interested."

Daniel sat down by her side and held her hand. Neither spoke for a long time.

Daniel knew he ought to say something definite about the future, but he simply did not know what to say. Grace waited patiently but her expectancy was not soon rewarded. The conversation, when it did start again, concerned itself with local matters—until the hour arrived for Daniel to return to Boscawen.

"My sister should be home soon," Grace's thoughts had turned to the parting. "Then you must go."

"Yes, I should like to take my farewell of your

family," Daniel returned. "Moreover, I do not like to go before I must."

"But you start at dawn tomorrow for Portsmouth, you told me."

Suddenly a picture formed in young Daniel's mind of riding, riding, riding away from Salisbury and Grace and all that he held dear.

He took both her hands in his and looked searchingly into her kind eyes.

"Oh, Grace, I shall return often to see you—and if you—if I— Oh, Grace, you must know what I am trying to say. When I have worked up a good practice in Portsmouth, would you—could you . . ."

"You know the answer, Daniel," she replied softly.

CHAPTER SEVEN

DANIEL MARRIES

FOR YEARS DANIEL HAD WANTED TO PRACTICE IN Portsmouth, the largest city in his native state. Often he had seen the great wharves crowded with ships from all over the world, waiting to take goods from New England to various ports. In these shipyards John Paul Jones' flagship, *The Ranger,* had been built.

It was an imposing town for the period; its industry and bustle were constant. As Daniel strolled down Market Street, he paused to take a second look at the home of General Whipple, who had signed the Declaration of Independence. He paused again on Pleasant Street in front of a fine house which he knew George Washington had called the handsomest in Portsmouth.

It would be difficult to get a foothold here, but not so difficult as in Boston or New York, he comforted himself. Like those cities it was a seaport, and Daniel loved the sea. The fishermen fascinated him; he longed to go out in a trawler with them and try his luck. The sailors, many of them from other countries, lent a gaiety to the scene which entranced the young man.

His own appearance was striking enough to make many a young lady half-turn her pretty head and glance from under her flower-bedecked bonnet. Slender, delicately formed for a young man, Daniel's massive brow and large black eyes had an immediate appeal. His features were unusual, his mouth well-formed and gentle, his general pallor accentuated by his raven-black hair.

Who was he? people wondered. Such a personable young man was an event, even in Portsmouth.

The mystery remained, even when—on the first Sunday after his arrival—he was placed by the sexton, as was customary at that time, in the minister's own pew. The minister, as it happened, was the father of young Reverend Buckminster who had received Daniel at Exeter, and who now was the minister of a fashionable church in Boston.

Daniel found the older Dr. Buckminster friendly toward him, and this at once put the town's stamp of approval on young Daniel Webster.

Daniel's spirit of fun delighted the Buckminster children. As he sat by their window, he would make up the most amusing and ridiculous stories about the people who were passing by, people about whom he actually knew nothing. When their mother came in to serve tea, she would find them all gathered around the dark young man, laughing loudly and gaily.

Dr. Buckminster took a fatherly interest. "Daniel," he said one day, "I want to suggest something to strengthen and fill out that slight figure of yours." He looked critically at Daniel's slender form. "You don't look as sturdy as I think you should," he continued. "What do you say to a little wood sawing before breakfast?"

Daniel was enthusiastic. "I'd like that, sir!"

"Splendid! Then we will start tomorrow. Don't fail me!"

Nor did he. Each morning Daniel walked over the lawn which separated his cottage from the parsonage, rolled up his sleeves, and he and the older man sawed wood for a couple of hours. On the first morning Daniel's face got redder and redder and perspiration began to run down his neck. He was chagrined to see that Dr. Buckminster showed no such signs of labor. But this did not deter him. He knew, too well, that all things were harder in the beginning. Ease and facility would come from practice.

It was the same with the law.

He had been hearing a lot about the nationally famous Jeremiah Mason, the greatest Common Law expert of his day. Daniel wondered if he would ever meet this lawyer, and perhaps even argue *against* the man. He would like to try his arguments; just possibly he could come out ahead.

But when at last Daniel was to appear as the opposing advocate to Jeremiah Mason, he was filled with endless doubts.

To be thus chosen was, of course, an honor. Daniel was conscious of this, although he also realized that there were not many other young lawyers with even his ability.

When he saw Jeremiah Mason in Court, the humor of his situation struck him so suddenly he could scarcely keep from laughing. Mr. Mason was a giant of a man, six-foot-seven in height; he made young

Daniel feel almost a dwarf. He had rarely seen anyone taller than Zeke and he had envied his brother his six foot ever since he could remember. Here was a man to tower over even Zeke! Mr. Mason was massive, too, with immense shoulders and head.

Daniel felt, he thought drolly, as David must have felt when he went against Goliath. He glanced up at the good-natured face, whose shrewdness was hidden behind a benign expression. His alert eyes were appraising Daniel, almost as if they wanted to say: "I can't help being so big. Don't mind that. We are here to measure our wits, not our bodies. Just see how you can win out there!"

In this first case Daniel took great pains to build up, detail by detail, an air-tight legal case for his client. In addressing the jury, he worked himself up into an emotional mood, using flowery and fiery phrases. He was rather pleased with himself when he finished.

"Then," as Daniel was later to tell Dr. Buckminster, "I saw Jeremiah Mason rise from his seat. He had been looking rather apathetic and sluggish, I thought, sitting through my summing-up; only now and then did he lift his brows and dart an alert glance toward me . . ."

"That's Jeremiah, right enough," chuckled Dr. Buckminster.

"Cool as you please, with slow, deliberate steps he approached the jury, looked kindly at them as a father might look at his children, whom he is about to instruct or admonish. Then conversationally, standing first near one, then another, without a single gesture, nor one colorful phrase, without once raising his voice, he explained his case to them." Daniel paused and looked about at his listeners.

"His very simplicity, the clear, straightforward way

he spoke carried its own conviction. It taught me a lesson, a lesson I needed to learn," Daniel explained.

Miss Buckminster smiled at the earnest young narrator.

"But who won the case?" her father asked.

"He did! How could he have helped it? He was so skillful, so much better in every way than I."

"But you told us you had a good case and made the most of it."

"I thought I did! It has taught me humility." Daniel felt better when he had said that.

"Mr. Mason was very generous," he added. "He congratulated me!"

" 'You put up a strong case, young man,' he said. 'I had to look smartly to win it. For awhile I thought I'd lost!' "

"That's a great compliment from Jeremiah Mason," Dr. Buckminster observed. "Why he's famous for his sharp tongue. Mr. Mason often speaks of this or that man as 'little Mr. Jones' or 'little Mr. Brown'; I wager he'll never say 'little Mr. Webster!' "

Often after that Daniel appeared against Mr. Mason; he studied the older man's technique and methods. This careful observation was now and again rewarded when Daniel won a case.

Mr. Mason didn't seem to mind in the least. In fact, Daniel sometimes suspected that he was pleased! It is never unpleasant to find a talented opponent studying your methods and emulating you, especially when you are so firmly established as to fear no rivals.

"Learn, learn . . ." the words of his father kept recurring to Daniel. Yes, he was willing to learn from Mr. Mason. He valued deeply the growing friendship which was developing between them. He knew his own reputation as a lawyer was growing, too. These two men so often appeared on opposite sides that Jeremiah Mason said to him in jest one day:

"Well, Mr. Webster, which side are you taking? Come, shall we toss a coin for it?"

Daniel, who knew Mr. Mason was fourteen years his senior, was honored to be considered his friend. Jeremiah once remarked that Daniel Webster had the makings of a great actor, and added that Daniel always played himself, his innermost self—a role of utter honesty and integrity. Daniel felt there was some truth in what his older friend said; some combination of gifts was giving him power over men. He was in increasing demand as a speaker at Fourth of July and other anniversary celebrations.

The legal work he was doing was arduous. He was not yet making a sufficient income to support a wife, but deep down his impatience was growing. He wanted Grace Fletcher at his side.

Of course they had been exchanging letters, but these were poor things compared to companionship. Finally he had a chance to see her again! The Circuit Court was making its rounds as usual, but now it was to be in the direction of Salisbury.

Daniel did what often had to be done by a lawyer in those days. From place to place he journeyed on horseback, since he could not afford a carriage. He usually traveled at night, and sometimes he went hungry before reaching an inn where he could get food and shelter at such inconvenient hours. "Riding the Circuit" this was then called.

Above all, he was happy that he would soon see Grace. At the morning session of the Court, he would make a plea for his client. Then in the afternoon and evening he would be free. Grace would be there to stroll beside him through the woods and meadows!

As he rode along he thought of that other horseback ride, just a few years ago, to Dartmouth. How much had happened since that remote day! Then he had been shy and uncertain of himself. Now he was a lawyer, advancing to better days, and, as he hoped, to fame. On this night he felt free and confident.

At Judge Kelley's house, the next afternoon, Grace herself opened the door.

"Why, Mr. Webster, it's wonderful to see you again! Come in! You'll stay awhile, I hope."

"Indeed I shall. I feel terribly audacious today, Grace. You must expect revelations."

"Revelations? You sound mysterious, Daniel." Grace smiled. "What is it, Daniel?" she asked as they sat down in the front parlor.

"All in good time, Grace. As the daughter of a minister, you must know that 'To everything there is a season, and a time to every purpose under the heaven . . . A time to be born, and a time to die . . . A time . . .'"

At this instant Judge Kelley and his wife entered. Daniel rose, blushing almost as vividly as Grace, and greeted them.

After dinner, Daniel and Grace walked down the footpath which led to the river. The sky was splashed with stars, and the moonlight shimmered on the little brook that ran through the meadow.

"'To everything there is a season,'" Daniel repeated. He took Grace's hand. "Can we marry soon?" he asked. "Next month at the latest?" He looked deeply into her eyes. "We shall be very poor at first, for I still must pay all my father's debts. But I am lonely, indescribably lonely in Portsmouth without you, Grace."

So in June, 1808, with only the two families present, Daniel and Grace were married in Judge Kelley's

house in Salisbury. After the ceremony they left at once for Portsmouth, where Daniel had leased a small but comfortable house for himself and his bride.

Daniel's friends in Portsmouth were surprised. They had not known that the young lawyer had any wedding plans. But they welcomed with pleasure the bride of Daniel Webster.

CHAPTER EIGHT

A CONGRESSMAN FROM NEW HAMPSHIRE

A FEW YEARS LATER DANIEL RUSHED INTO HIS bright and cheerful parlor, singing gaily.

"Prepare for guests, Grace!" he called. "I met young George Ticknor, who's visiting here in Portsmouth, and asked him and his friend to come to dinner tonight."

"How delightful!" Grace exclaimed. "I remember Mr. Ticknor from our first trip to Hanover, after our marriage. He was a student at Dartmouth."

"That's right. And it was on that trip that I expressed my literary ideas before Phi Beta Kappa."

"Do you recall, Daniel, how amused Mr. Mason was when you said: 'Rome got out of her cradle an infant savage with all the wolf in her blood?'"

"Not like this country of ours," Daniel laughed gaily. "We had scholars for our first colonists!"

Daniel threw his arm around his wife and turned her

toward the window. There sat their two-year-old daughter, Grace, looking at a picture.

"You see I was right, Grace. Even our infants are scholars!"

"Look, this is Jesus," the child pointed to the colored picture. "See, the little girl's just like me. Jesus is saying: 'Suffer little children to come unto me and forbid them not . . . for such is the kingdom of heaven.'" She smiled up at her parents.

Daniel clasped the child in his arms. Handing the picture to her mother, he perched his daughter on his shoulder and danced her up and down, while she shouted with delight.

"What a memory our little Grace has, what a memory she has!" he chanted, as he pranced about.

"She really has, Daniel. It's several days since I explained that picture to her." Grace's face was filled with pride.

Daniel awakened his wife the next morning, calling from the door:

"'The east is bright with morning light,
  Uprose the king of men with speed . . .'"

Quickly dressing, Grace was soon at his side.

"Why, Daniel!" she exclaimed. "I do believe you haven't been in bed at all!"

Daniel looked down at his wrinkled clothing and admitted he had fallen asleep while working.

"I was writing a paper I'm addressing to President Madison. Scarcely realizing how late it was and how tired I was, I must have dropped to sleep at my desk."

"Mr. Madison's War is troubling us in New England in more ways than one," observed Grace with a sympathetic smile. "I hope the President will pay some attention to us. I was pleased when you were appointed head of the Rockingham assembly and chosen to write the paper to the President."

"I trust they won't be disappointed in their choice," said Daniel. "I have urged immediate naval preparations and made recommendations for a peace. I'll read you a bit of it, if you want me to."

"I shall know every word by heart before long," his wife replied.

Daniel raised the sheets of paper he was holding, and read aloud:

"We are, sir, from principle and habit, attached to the Union of the States. But our attachment is to the substance and not to the form. It is to the good this Union is capable of producing, and not to the evil which is suffered unnaturally to grow out of it . . ."

Grace's approval of her young husband's efforts was hardly less enthusiastic than the Assembly's. Daniel Webster was elected from Rockingham county to the Congress in Washington. This was what his father had wanted for him.

When Daniel left Portsmouth in May to attend the special session in Washington, his father was much in his thoughts.

He was back in Portsmouth by midsummer when a son, Daniel Fletcher Webster, was born to him. His happiness was now overflowing.

The night before he returned to Washington, he heard someone singing in his infant son's room. Opening the door softly, he saw little Grace, raised on tiptoe, gently rocking the baby's cradle, while she sang:

"'Hush, my dear, lie still and slumber;
    Holy angels guard thy bed,

> Heavenly blessings without number
> Gently falling on thy head.'"

Suddenly the child spied him; she ran barefooted to him, and threw her arms about his knees.

"Come, Grace, you must go to your own bed. You'll take cold running about, and if you don't go to sleep you'll feel tired tomorrow." He led her to the adjoining small room.

"Now say a prayer, sweetheart."

The child knelt beside her bed and closed her eyes as she prayed:

> "'Matthew, Mark, Luke and John
> God bless the bed which I lie on,
> Four angels round me spread,
> Two at my feet and two at my head.'"

Then she climbed into bed and said solemnly, "Those four angels won't let anything happen to me—not ever."

Daniel sat quietly in a chair beside her bed. Soon his daughter was sound asleep.

During the congressional sessions of 1813-14, Daniel boarded at Crawford's Hotel in Georgetown. Always at the head of the dinner table sat old Christopher Gore, who had first insisted Daniel complete his legal training. Mr. Gore had been Governor of Massachusetts and now was a Senator from that state. Daniel's old friend Jeremiah Mason was also a Senator. He, too, sat at the table, as did Rufus King, the Senator from New York, and many other well-known men. It was a world without ladies, except for the receptions at the White House.

Hardly had he arrived in Washington when news reached him of the great Portsmouth fire—two-hundred and forty buildings destroyed and some fifteen acres charred and ruined.

Daniel's house, which he had just bought, and his library, which he had been collecting for many years, were completely destroyed. He carried no insurance, so it was a great financial loss to him; but he was so relieved that his wife and children had escaped unharmed and to learn that they were temporarily housed at Mr. Mason's, that he felt less concern about his material loss.

To make up his losses and earn extra money which his growing family made necessary, Daniel decided to return to his legal practice, after his term was over.

A little after this he moved to Boston, going first to Mrs. Delano's for a few weeks, then moving into the house he had chosen on Mount Vernon Street. This house, too, belonged to Jeremiah Mason.

Their faithful servant Hannah accompanied them. After they were settled, Daniel asked Grace to go to Washington with him. He would finish his term with the autumn.

Before he left home, he heard sad news from Zeke. Zeke's little daughter, Mary, had died. And it was scarcely five years, Daniel recollected, since his younger sister, Sally, had died. The Boscawen Websters were having more than their share of sorrow, Daniel mused, as he sat watching his two healthy children at play.

Presently six-year-old Grace left her three-year-old brother and took one of her books to a stool near the fire. She loved to read. Daniel marveled at her intelligence and her sweetness.

That afternoon, his wife had told him, a beggar, more unclean and dangerous looking than most, had been brought to the kitchen by Grace.

Hannah, usually willing to feed all the beggars little Grace brought to her kitchen, was not so happy about it this time. She tried to refuse, but the child's eyes filled with tears.

"There just isn't enough food in the house, my dear child," insisted Hannah.

"I'm not hungry tonight. Please, oh, please, let the poor man have my dinner," Grace begged.

"Run along and get him some cold meat," Hannah capitulated. "We'll both likely have to go without our suppers, but that's better than tears."

Gently little Grace served the surly man. Hannah marveled to see his savage, unshaven face grow softer. He was looking almost gentle by the time the little child brought him a second cup of coffee.

"She's an angel," the man had muttered as he left. "That child's too good for this world!"

The words left Hannah quite unstrung. She had thought recently that Grace didn't look as well as usual. Since her little cousin Mary died, Hannah had worried a good deal about Grace. They had often played together and people did say consumption was catching, Hannah thought to herself.

Mrs. Webster was delighted to be in Washington with her husband. But as soon as she was there, she began to worry about little Grace. She had planned to stay a few months, but she had been there only a few weeks when they received alarming news from Boston: little Grace was ill! Daniel decided they should both rush back at once.

They found the child very ill, and the doctor said it was consumption. She coughed until she was exhausted, but she never complained.

Young Daniel Fletcher was the picture of health. He

was delighted to have his parents home again and insisted that Daniel help him make a snow man. When the snow figure was completed, Daniel hastened upstairs to lift Grace to the window where she might see it.

"Isn't it a splendid snow man, Father? Soon I'll be well again and then you'll make one for me, won't you?"

"Indeed I shall, my darling," Daniel replied. He tried to smile, but tears filled his eyes.

Each day little Grace grew weaker. Each night Daniel and Grace, their hands tightly clasped together, sat by her bedside. The doctor held out no hope for recovery.

One night when her cough had been somewhat less frequent, she fell into a gentle sleep. Daniel and his wife took time to get a much needed rest.

Hannah came to the door of their room. "She's awake and asking for you, sir," she said in a low voice.

"Don't disturb Mrs. Webster," Daniel returned in a whisper. "She's exhausted. I'll go to her, Hannah." He hastened to the child's room.

Little Grace greeted him with a sweet smile. He put his arm beneath her and drew her gently to him. Her face was suffused with love. She died so quietly he scarcely knew when she stopped breathing.

Then Daniel put his head in his hands and cried as if his heart had broken.

CHAPTER NINE

PRACTICE BEFORE THE U.S.
SUPREME COURT

DANIEL WEBSTER WAS SUPREME AS AN ADVOCATE and lawyer, from the time he pleaded his first great case before the highest court in the land, until the end of his long life.

At the time of his first great case, Daniel was a young man of thirty-six. His extremely high forehead was crowned with thick jet-black hair, worn somewhat long; his sideburns reached to the neck. He still had the slenderness of youth. His mouth was gentle and sweet, not the firm line it became in later years. In his buff waistcoat and dark blue coat with the white neck-cloth and ruffled shirt, he was extraordinarily handsome.

The case, known as Dartmouth College versus Woodward (1819), had been decided against Mr. Mason and Mr. Webster in New Hampshire courts; it was

67

now before the Supreme Court in Washington. The trouble had been smouldering underground for a couple of decades before it burst into the courts. It was mixed up with differences in religions and with differences as to the election of the President. The dissatisfactions grew and grew; soon everyone seemed to take sides.

Daniel had all the material used in New Hampshire to help him prepare his case. Yet he was doubtful of his ability to win; again and again he tried to escape from the trial.

But when he finally addressed the Supreme Court his argument was perfect. He spoke for hours, bringing to his plea Roman law, English law, quoting great judges and classical lawyers. He built the case up stone by stone, so firmly, so tightly, that it was a perfect structure of its kind.

Before the Supreme Court of the United States, headed by the great John Marshall, he showed himself to be a creative artist. Jeremiah Mason had often said young Daniel was a fine actor. He proved it on this day. He not only composed the piece, but he acted out the leading part, carrying his audience along with him.

On the day of the trial the small room was crowded, mostly with distinguished lawyers from all parts of the country. Young Rufus Choate, who was to become a famous lawyer, orator, and statesman, decided to study law after he heard Daniel Webster on that memorable day.

When the small back door opened and the Chief Justice stepped through, followed by the other members of the Court in their black silk robes, Daniel did not suspect that he was about to make history.

The Court crier announced: "The honorable, the Supreme Court of the United States is now in session . . .

God save the United States and this honorable Court."

The Chief Justice seated himself. John Marshall was one of the most famous men in the country. He had been impressed with Daniel Webster when he first read his congressional efforts. For three hours that day he sat as if mesmerized, scarcely moving, never taking his eyes from young Webster.

Mr. Justice Story, Daniel's friend from Massachusetts, sat with his quill pen suspended over the blank sheets of notepaper he had brought with him. He did not write a word. His friend Webster was so lucid, as he made point after point, so clear in his legal reasoning as to make note-taking superfluous.

Daniel argued that Dartmouth College was a private corporation and that a charter or franchise was also a contract. This, he argued, could not be modified without the consent of both parties.

By the end of the fourth hour Daniel turned to the hardships, the heartaches of the poor. He said he himself had been a poor boy; he knew what it was to go to college with a few pennies only. He spoke of the pioneers who struggled to raise their children to a less hard life than their own; he thought of his own father and what he had done for Zeke and himself. He spoke from the depths of his heart.

He extolled Dr. Eleazor Wheelock. This man had loved the Indians; he had loved poor boys. His school had been started for these. When this good man died his son had followed loyally in his footsteps.

Think of the sufferings of those poor boys, how they struggled to obtain an education, he cried, think of it!

Many of the ladies in the courtroom were crying. Even the kind eyes of the Chief Justice were bright with tears.

"It is, sir, as I have said, a small college. And yet

there are those who love it," here Daniel's voice broke, his lips quivered.

He was now possessed by his subject as his audience was possessed by him. Four hours lengthened to four and a half. Still he spoke on. His own eyes filled with tears that flowed down his cheeks.

Sobs could be heard from his entranced audience, as he launched into his final words.

"Sir," he addressed himself to the Chief Justice, "I know not how others may feel," he glanced at the opposing lawyers. "But for myself, when I see my Alma Mater surrounded like Caesar in the Senate-house by those who are reiterating stab after stab, I would not, for this right hand, have her turn to me and say, 'Et tu quoque mi fili!'" (And thou, too, my son).

Daniel Webster sat down.

Nobody moved. There was complete silence.

The ticking of the clock was strangely loud; minutes passed. The scene this Court had witnessed was amazing; they had been raised to such a pitch of excitement, their emotions had been so stirred and tormented that the most reserved had found it impossible to conceal their agitation. Clenched hands and tense expressions revealed their anxiety.

The Chief Justice arose, followed by the other six; they left the room by the doorway they had entered.

Daniel himself went to his lodgings and was soon writing to Jeremiah Mason and Zeke. How he hoped these two men would approve what he had done! It was his best, he knew. But had he won?

Rumor had it that the Chief Justice and two others favored his side of the case, but four of the seven were needed. Would there be a fourth? It was almost a half year before he knew the decision—he had triumphed!

Daniel had now moved his family into a house on Somerset Street in Boston. Here a second son, Edward, was born to them. A year after the death of his beloved little Grace, another daughter had been born. This was Julia, who had such enormous dark eyes that everyone who saw her commented on them.

One afternoon in early autumn Daniel's friends, the George Ticknors and the Jeremiah Masons, had come for dinner. He and the men retired to his private sitting room to discuss political matters.

Grace was chatting with the ladies when she heard an odd noise from the hallway. It sounded as if something were falling plop, plop, very slowly down the stairs. She quickly excused herself and hurried to the hallway, where she met Mr. Mason who was about to join the ladies.

On the stairway, about halfway down, was young Daniel Fletcher with a white bundle in his arms. Grace knew at once that the bundle was her newborn baby, Edward. Her heart stood still.

Slowly with infinite care, young Fletcher, his eyes intent on the stair next below him, came down another step. Just then the embroidery on the bottom of the baby's long dress caught in his shoe.

He swayed . . . and swayed again.

Grace was trembling so violently she thought she would fall. Mr. Mason reached out and supported her, whispering:

"Don't make a sound. You'll startle him."

Breathless they watched the boy regain his balance and proceed slowly and carefully to the foot of the stairs. Now his mother quickly approached him and gathered her precious baby in her arms.

Grace was so overwrought that Mr. Mason sum-

moned Daniel. Soon Daniel joined the ladies and found
Fletcher curled up at the feet of young Mrs. Ticknor.

"Don't be cross with him," she begged Daniel, as she
stroked the boy's fair hair. "He meant no harm."

"Come, Fletcher," was Daniel's only reply. "I must
see you privately."

The seven-year-old boy followed his father to an un-
occupied room.

"Now tell me all about it," said Daniel kindly.

"Oh, sir, I wouldn't hurt Edward for anything. I was
very careful. I just wanted to show him to the ladies.
He is so sweet I knew they would want to see him, and
Mother . . ."

"We aren't discussing your mother," Daniel interrupted more severely. "I understand from your Uncle
Paige and from Hannah that you have often taken Edward from his cradle."

"But never from his room," protested the lad.

"Because someone always stopped you!" Daniel
looked very seriously at his young son. "You must never
again take baby Edward from his cradle."

He took Fletcher's hands in his and pressed them
with all his strength, looking sternly into the young
eyes so like his wife's. He remained thus for several
minutes. Then he let his son go without another word.

Young Fletcher knew that he would never again lift
his baby brother out of his cradle. If he even considered such a thing, his father's black eyes would be
piercing into his very thoughts and he would never be
able to do it.

One winter day, Daniel and Grace and some friends
set off for Plymouth, where Daniel was to speak at the
celebration commemorating the 200th anniversary of
the landing of the Pilgrims.

When they reached Plymouth that evening, the town

had the air of a fête. All the houses were illuminated; a band of musicians marched up and down, followed by a cheering crowd.

The next morning Daniel and George Ticknor went early to the church where Daniel was to later give the oration. It was the old First Church, of which Dr. Kendall was the minister.

Daniel did not find the pulpit in a convenient location. "It is far too high, too far from the people," Daniel insisted.

He tried out one position after another. Finally he decided to speak from the Deacon's seat under the pulpit. One of the men brought him a table. He suggested it be covered, so a green baize cloth was placed over the table. The arrangement seemed rather odd to Mr. Ticknor, but he decided not to mention this to anyone but his wife.

When the procession had formed, they marched through the crowded streets and entered the church, followed by a throng of citizens. As they crowded in, Mr. Ticknor saw that Daniel had chosen his position well for speaking.

He spoke for about an hour. First he spoke of the need of property; he wanted every American to own his own property. He spoke of the Pilgrims who had been attached to the land of their adoption, because each had the opportunity to become a property owner.

Next he attacked slavery. He thundered at the manufacturers who made the manacles and fetters to be clasped around the innocent black limbs.

"It is not fit," he proclaimed, "that the land of the Pilgrims should bear this shame longer."

As he went on, he became more and more animated. When he reached his final thoughts, he spread his arms wide as if in welcome to future generations:

"We bid you welcome to this pleasant land of the fathers. We bid you welcome to the healthful skies and verdant fields of New England . . . We welcome you to the blessings of good government and religious liberty. We welcome you to the treasures of science and the delights of learning . . . We welcome you to the immeasurable blessings of rational existence, the immortal hope of Christianity, and the light of everlasting truth!"

When the Websters finally returned to their lodgings, immense crowds followed them. Daniel was radiant with happiness; his wife's eyes were shining with pride.

Young George Ticknor turned to his wife. "There's something very grand and imposing about Daniel Webster," he said with admiration. "He seems to be like the mount that might not be touched, and that burns with fire!"

The great public dinner was followed by a ball. Daniel was affable and charming. Only when he and his friends finally returned to their lodgings did he become as frolicsome as a schoolboy, talking and laughing continually.

The next day on the long drive back to Boston, Daniel went on talking, telling his friends odd and fascinating things about the Pilgrims.

Grace was very quiet. She was tired out by the unusual emotional experience. Her thoughts now flew to her children. She was never wholly content when she was not with them.

CHAPTER TEN

CONGRESSMAN FROM MASSACHUSETTS

W HEN DANIEL ARRIVED IN WASHINGTON AS CON-
gressman from Massachusetts, his position was
no longer that of a young novice. His practice
before the Supreme Court and his famous oratory at
Plymouth, as well as endless other public speeches,
had made his name known from one end of the country
to the other. He now felt it was his duty to address
Congress on some subject.

At this time Greece was fighting a war of independence from Turkish domination. Because of his love of
the classics, this struggle attracted Daniel. The cause
of the Greeks and their appeal to his own country, the
one existing republic, touched him. He felt this appeal
should not go unanswered.

"Don't you think it a good idea for me to say something about the Greeks?" he said to his old friend, Edward Everett, one evening.

"No one can do it better," Mr. Everett answered
promptly. "You know that."

"The miserable issue of the Spanish revolution makes the Greek cause more interesting," Daniel went on. "I begin to think they have character enough to carry them through the contest with success."

"My first article on the Greeks will appear in the *North American Review* for October," Mr. Everett said. "If you like I can send it to you."

When Daniel read this essay he instantly wrote Edward Everett that he had enjoyed his admirable article and asked for more information. Mr. Everett sent him two manuscripts, maps, and all he could obtain relative to the Greeks. Another article by Mr. Everett was scheduled for publication in January.

When Daniel finally addressed Congress, crowds gathered, expecting a great oration. He may have disappointed them.

He made a great speech, but his object was something more than merely to express his warm sympathy with the fighting Greeks. He laid down principles for a lasting peace and reviewed the entire historical situation in some detail. Congress, however, while it admired his oratory, feared the country might become embroiled in war, so it all came to nothing.

Daniel was glad to return to Boston. By now he had a third son, Charles, who week by week grew to look more like his father. Perhaps for this reason, perhaps because he was the baby, both Grace and Daniel were particularly fond of the gay little fellow, who was just learning to lisp his first words and take his first steps that summer.

In the autumn, while driving Grace back to Boston from Cape Cod—the children having gone in another carriage with Hannah—Daniel chanced to take a road which ran past the Thomas farm.

As they descended into the valley, Grace was delighted with the beauty and quiet of the scene.

"Oh, Daniel," she begged, "please, please, stop here."

Daniel drew up at the gate, which read "Marshfield."

"Do drive in and see who lives in this delightful place," Grace urged.

When the owners found that the famous Daniel Webster was outside, they were warmly hospitable. They even implored Mr. and Mrs. Webster to return and make a short visit.

Daniel could not bear to leave. The sea, the sea, how he loved the sea! And it was less than a mile away! Grace, too, could hardly tear herself away from the beautiful valley.

As they drove along toward Boston, Daniel told her, "I made arrangements to return with the children every summer. It is already our home. As soon as I possibly can, I shall buy it. But never will I let the Thomases leave. We shall share it with them as long as they live."

"Oh, Daniel, I think it is the most perfect old farmhouse I've ever seen. I can scarcely wait to tell the children the good news!"

Daniel Webster was anxious to meet Thomas Jefferson. So the following December, with Mr. and Mrs. George Ticknor, he left Washington to visit Jefferson at Monticello. They took a steamboat to Fredericksburg Landing, and then continued in a carriage with four horses. The roads were bad, and it was long after dark when they reached their first stopping place.

Daniel was in a gay mood and kept his friends entertained with excellent stories. He even sang old songs and acted as irresponsible as a boy.

They next stopped to see Mr. Madison, the former President of the United States; he was an old friend of Daniel's. The following day, Daniel and George Ticknor took a horseback ride of eight or ten miles through woods and across fields; Daniel was as merry as he had been the previous day.

The Marshfield farm at Green Harbor was constantly in his thoughts. Daniel broke forth so often in the haunting strains of "Home Sweet Home" that George Ticknor finally asked:

"Did you see *Clari, or, the Maid of Milan* in New York last year?"

"No," Daniel replied with a smile. "But Grace and I have better reason to know the inner meaning of that song than Mr. Payne who wrote it. Poor fellow, he has no Marshfield!"

Again they dined with Mr. Madison, who told many entertaining stories. These delighted Daniel, who found those jokes with a political twist particularly amusing. After this intimate contact, he decided that Mr. Madison was indeed the wisest of all former Presidents, with the exception of Washington.

The thirty-two miles from Mr. Madison's to Mr. Jefferson's occupied them more than a day. At Mrs. Clarke's Tavern, where they stopped, Daniel said, "You may think me foolishly gay, but the truth is I have not felt so free from care and anxiety for five years."

The very next day, however, he received a letter from Grace which deeply disturbed him. She wrote that little Charles had been taken ill, very ill.

They were welcomed at Monticello by Thomas Jefferson, who rode out to meet them. He wore a gray straight-bodied coat and a long spencer of the same color. About his neck he had wound a white woollen tippet. He had added black velvet gaiters to guard his feet.

At this time he was a man in his early eighties, but full of vivacity and spirit. His once-red hair had now a sandy hue, while his skin was badly marked by age. His hands and feet were very large, even out of proportion to his stature.

He was in excellent health. He achieved this, he said, by the regularity of his life. "I rise," he told his guests, "as soon as I can distinguish the hands of my clock, and employ myself in writing until breakfast, which I have at nine. On fair mornings I ride ten to fourteen miles; when the weather is bad I employ myself in my library. I dine at four. At six I retire to my drawing room, where I enjoy conversation until nine. At nine I retire for the night."

At home he wore a dark gray surtout coat and pantaloons of the same color, a kerseymere yellow waistcoat, with an under-waistcoat of a dingy red. His dress was obviously neglected.

For three days Mr. Jefferson talked with his visitors about his former friends, telling delightful stories about many of them.

As he listened, Daniel would lean back on the sofa and shake with laughter. He, too, told some stories; and since he was particularly fond of jokes on himself, one story he told was at his own expense:

"One night recently, Mr. Jefferson, I was forced to make a journey by private carriage from Baltimore to Washington. The man who drove was an ill-looking fellow who told story after story of robberies and murders, until I was painfully uneasy.

"Finally," said Daniel, after a pause, "he stopped the carriage in the midst of a dense wood. I was almost frightened out of my wits!" Daniel's eyes twinkled. "The man turned to me and demanded fiercely: 'Now, sir, tell me who you are!' Making ready to spring from my conveyance, I stammered out in a faltering voice: 'I am Daniel Webster, Member of Congress from Massachusetts.' 'What!' exclaimed the driver, grasping me warmly by the hand. 'Are you Webster? Thank goodness! You are such an ugly fellow, I took you for a cutthroat or a highwayman!'"

By the third day Daniel had become restless. He had enjoyed seeing the University Mr. Jefferson had founded, and also enjoyed talking with the famous President. But he was worried about little Charles.

Rain detained them for a fourth day. By now Daniel was even more restless. He was very anxious for news of the sick child. On the return journey Daniel was depressed—impatient to hear, yet fearful of what he would hear.

When he reached Washington, there was no news from Boston. Was no news good news? Devoutly Daniel hoped it was.

It was a letter from his brother-in-law, William Paige, that finally told him little Charles was dead!

There was nothing he could do. Nothing. It was all over. Long before he heard, little Charles lay with his sister Grace in St. Paul's.

Grace wrote to try to cheer her husband; Daniel wrote to his beloved wife for the same reason.

From his youngest days, Daniel had often written verses. Now he wrote nine verses of four lines each, which he called "Lines on the Death of Our Son, Charles":

> My son, thou wast my heart's delight,
> Thy morn of life was gay and cheery;

That morn has rushed to sudden night,
Thy father's house is sad and dreary.

I held thee on my knee, my son!
And kissed thee laughing, kissed thee weeping;
But ah! thy little day is done,
Thou'rt with thy angel sister sleeping.

.   .   .

Sweet seraph, I would learn of thee,
And hasten to partake thy bliss!
And oh! to thy world welcome me,
As first I welcomed thee to this.

Dear Angel, thou art safe in heaven:
No prayers for thee need be made;
Oh! let thy prayers for those be given
Who oft have blessed thy infant head.

CHAPTER ELEVEN

TWO GREAT ORATIONS

EARLY ONE SUMMER MORNING DANIEL SET OUT FROM the stagecoach inn at Sandwich to fish in the Marshpee, below Wakeby Pond. He was accompanied by his twelve-year-old son, Daniel Fletcher, and a friend whom he had nicknamed "John Trout."

The Marshpee, a short, rapid stream, ran in a deep ravine with steep hills on either side. These hillocks were covered with a thick growth of small pines, brushwood, and shrubs.

Right down the middle of the dashing stream waded Daniel and John Trout, followed closely by the young boy. As the morning hours passed, Fletcher observed that his father displayed less interest than usual in his favorite sport. Daniel was letting his line run carelessly downstream and he ignored the best spots under the projecting pine roots.

"Father, your hook is hanging on a twig," young Daniel Fletcher called.

84

Daniel removed the hook, only to allow it to get caught in the long grass.

"Careful, Father," the boy again warned. "You won't get any trout if you leave your hook there."

Young Fletcher had by then caught up with Daniel, and he now was sure his father was paying no attention to his fishing tackle. Instead, he was gazing up into overhanging trees!

Fletcher was puzzled, but before he could speak again, his father said in a loud voice:

"Venerable men! Venerable men!"

After a pause, he repeated "Venerable men!" and launched into a version of the speech he was soon to deliver at Bunker Hill. "You have come down to us from former generations. Heaven has bounteously lengthened your lives that you might behold this joyous day . . ."

In Boston, when that "joyous day" arrived, Daniel was still uncomfortable about his oration. He felt certain he could speak to the survivors of the Revolution, for had not his own father been such a man? But how could he do justice to the great hero, Lafayette, who was to be the guest of honor? How could he find the auspicious words for this? What if he should not be able to fulfill the expectations of his friends and fellow-countrymen?

When the procession was formed at the Senate House, the military contingents were in full uniform, and banners and badges were seen everywhere. There were two hundred veterans of the American Revolution, forty of whom had actually been on Breed's Hill on that memorable day in 1775. Shouting, cheering multitudes followed them through the streets.

The procession slowly wound its way from the Boston Common across the Charles River bridge and halted at Breed's Hill, where the cornerstone of the monument was laid with masonic ceremonies. On Bunker Hill itself, more than twenty thousand persons had congregated. People had poured in from all parts of the country. Temporary seats for several thousand had been erected on the side of the hill; the platform from which Daniel spoke was at the bottom.

But so clear and full, so rich and resonant, was Daniel Webster's voice that it even reached the listeners at the brow of the famous hill.

The words about the rising of the monument, the eloquence addressed to the old soldiers of Bunker Hill, the apostrophe to General Warren, the superb tribute he paid to Lafayette in which he said he was only "reluctant to grant our highest and last honors to the living, honors we would gladly hold yet back from the little remnant of the immortal band," brought forth such cheers, such prolonged shouts, that it seemed to Daniel they would never end.

At one time, some of the seats and barriers gave way, causing great confusion.

"It is impossible to restore order, Mr. Webster," an attendant told him.

"Nothing is impossible, sir," replied Webster with great severity. "Let it be done."

Silence was finally restored and Daniel continued his interrupted oration. When he reached his last words, his voice rang with a clarion call:

"Let our object be our country, our whole country, and nothing but our country!"

That night he held a reception for General Lafayette, and the crowds were so great that they overflowed into his neighbor's house in Summer Street. Earlier in the week, Colonel Thorndyke, his neighbor, had cut a

passage through the wall from his house to Daniel's, so the guests might spread out in both homes.

Nonetheless, Daniel was still troubled about the wording of his oration and remained troubled during his trip to Niagara with his wife and friends. He returned from the Falls to find the country ringing with his praises and to learn that his speech had been translated into French and other European languages. Even so, he wished he had had more time to polish it. He went on striving to equal or excel the hero of his youth, Cicero.

Again he spent the summer and part of the autumn with his family in Sandwich, on Cape Cod. When he had to return to Washington, Grace and the children accompanied him.

The morning after the dinner with President and Mrs. John Quincy Adams, the Webster family was gathered at the breakfast table.

"Tell us about the dinner, Mother, please," urged eight-year-old Julia.

"Mrs. Adams looked lovely, dear, and the President was very kind. We didn't have to shiver and shake in an enormous, cold room, either! We were shown into a small, warm parlor!"

"Then you didn't need the extra cloak Father made you take?" Fletcher asked.

"No, my son. Nor did I need an overcoat!" Daniel said. "We had a very good dinner, and a very good time. But, as you know, I haven't any great liking for large dinner parties."

"I'm certain Mother and the ladies like them," observed little Edward, who was five.

"But you know, I think they're no better for the presence of ladies, Edward!" retorted Daniel, laughing.

"You shouldn't say that, Father! Every party is nicer if my Mother is there," Edward insisted, as he filled his mouth with a slice of bread and jam.

"What a pretty compliment, my dear," Daniel looked affectionately at Grace.

"Edward is a good son," Grace said tenderly. "You mustn't spoil him with praise."

She rose from the table. "I have so many duties to perform this morning, I must ask to be excused."

"I wish you'd stay home with me," Edward pleaded. "Or let me go with you."

"Why, Edward, what ails you today?" Daniel turned to his young son. "You know that is impossible! You must learn what is impossible, as early as you can. Then you will not be made unhappy so often."

It troubled Daniel later when he thought he had perhaps spoken too sternly to his youngest son, whom he loved dearly. He must, somehow, make it up to him. He would buy a present for the boy.

When on July Fourth, John Adams, the second President of the United States, died at Quincy, Massachusetts, and Thomas Jefferson, the third President of the United States, died at Monticello, Daniel Webster was as much struck by the astonishing coincidence as were the rest of his countrymen.

The two old men died within a few hours of each other. Both had been members of the Continental Congress and on the committee to frame the Declaration of Independence. One had written that great document; the other had been its foremost defender. Both had signed the famous declaration.

Strangest of all, this Fourth of July was the fiftieth anniversary of the adoption of the Declaration of Independence!

Commemorative services were held throughout the country. Daniel was chosen by Boston to deliver an oration in Faneuil Hall on August 2nd. This date was chosen because it was the fiftieth anniversary of the day that the copy of the world-renowned document was laid on the table of Congress to be signed.

One day, not long before the appointed date, Daniel rose very early. He looked long at the slowly brightening sky; the sun was just coming into view over the horizon. Then he sat down at his desk and wrote steadily for hours. When he finished, the paper was wet with his own tears. He had known both Presidents.

An immense number of people came to hear him speak at Faneuil Hall, which for the first time in history was draped in black. On the platform sat distinguished guests from all over New England.

When the doors were closed for the service, crowds were shut out. These crowds began to make so much noise that it was difficult to proceed within. Finally, Daniel perceived that some action must be taken. He strode to the front of the platform and shouted:

"Let those doors be opened!"

He was obeyed. A rush followed, then presently all was quiet again.

For the occasion Daniel Webster wore knee britches and an orator's gown. He had never looked handsomer, and his bearing expressed dignity and power. Although his manuscript lay on a small table near him, he did not once refer to it.

His speech was in two parts—the first purporting to be by an opponent of the Declaration, and the second was given as though Mr. Adams himself was replying.

Daniel's manner was deliberate and commanding. At one point in the speech, he stamped his foot and his form seemed to expand, as he spoke the words: "It is action, noble, sublime, godlike action!" His listeners were spellbound and thought him the very personification of the great men about whom he spoke.

CHAPTER TWELVE

SENATOR FROM MASSACHUSETTS

THE FOLLOWING YEAR DANIEL AND HIS FAMILY spent the summer as usual on Cape Cod—at Marshfield and at Sandwich.

While they were there, Daniel heard of a new fishing spot not more than ten miles from Marshfield. He was impatient to try his luck. So one morning he set out with young Fletcher, who was an enthusiastic fishing companion.

"Well," Daniel greeted the owner of the property on which the brook was located, "with your leave we would like to take a trout from your brook."

"Oh, yes, sir, you're very welcome to."

"I've heard there is very good fishing here," Daniel went on.

"Well, a good many folks have been here and taken out a good many trout, sometimes."

"We must try and see what we can do this morning. Where do they usually begin to fish?" Daniel asked.

93

"Oh, I'll show you."

The old man led Daniel and Fletcher to the brook, which was thickly overhung with alders. The ground was so miry that Daniel sank halfway up his legs.

"Rather miry here," he observed.

"Yes, that's the worst on't," replied the owner.

While Fletcher watched, Daniel threw his line several times, but it always caught in the alders.

"These alders are rather in the way," Daniel said laughingly.

"I know it; that's the worst on't," the old man said solemnly.

Fletcher began to unload his fishing tackle and prepare his own line. But he hesitated to try his own casting among so many trees. Perhaps he'd better watch for the next few minutes, he thought to himself.

By now swarms of mosquitoes were biting Daniel and Fletcher. Daniel would slap them off his face with one hand, while he grasped his fishing pole with the other.

"These mosquitoes are pretty thick and very hungry," Daniel observed.

"I know it; that's the worst on't."

By now the heat had become suffocating. Daniel wiped his forehead and decided to rest a few minutes. So far he hadn't had even a nibble.

"It's very hot down here in these bushes," he remarked.

The old man nodded sympathetically. "I know it; that's the worst on't."

Daniel soon resumed his fishing and urged his young son to try his luck. After an hour without a bite on either hook, they decided to stop.

"There seem to be no fish here," Daniel admitted sadly.

"I know it," returned the old man, who had stood beside the Websters throughout the heat, the mire, and the mosquitoes. "That's the worst on't."

By now Daniel could hardly keep from laughing. He put up his rod and prepared to leave. Fletcher was snickering as they said good-by to the owner of the place, but Daniel managed to keep a straight face.

As soon as they were in the carriage headed for home, he burst out in loud guffaws, punctuating his laughter with "that's the worst on't." He imitated perfectly the old man's voice, and Fletcher roared with delight.

It was a gay and happy summer, even though Grace's health gave Daniel some concern. But when they returned to Boston he was greatly cheered; Grace looked better than she had for several years.

The news of his appointment to the Senate, to fill the place of a sick Senator, had greatly pleased his wife. She now felt that no office in the country was too high for her husband to reach.

Grace planned to accompany him to Washington, and was occupied with happy plans for the winter. However, the journey to New York tired her; so Daniel insisted they stop over and consult Dr. Post, a well-known specialist.

Dr. Post advised Grace to return to Boston. He thought a winter in Washington society would be far too much for her.

So it was arranged that her brother William would come in a few days to take Grace back to Boston.

"What I dislike most," she told Daniel one day, "is keeping you from your work in Washington. Now that you are in the Senate, your presence there is of the utmost importance." She adjusted the shawl about her shoulders. "I did want to hear you speak in the Senate," she said softly.

"You will, my beloved wife, I feel confident you will." Daniel tried to put all his strength and faith into his voice. He had been greatly disturbed by Dr. Post's diagnosis.

The next two or three days Grace was so much better that Daniel felt hopeful. Then she seemed to develop a cold. Her limbs felt stiff and she was again in great pain, which she tried to conceal from her anxious husband.

Again, however, her condition improved so markedly after a few days that Daniel decided to go on to Washington.

"Don't worry about me at all," Grace said as he told her good-by. "I have my brother William to do everything needed."

"Dr. and Mrs. Perkins will take great care of you, I know," he replied, clasping her hand. "Here in their house, with William to do errands and look after the children when they come, you can lack nothing. And yet I do wish I could remain here by your side where I want to be."

The next month Grace unexpectedly became worse. Daniel rushed back to New York. He hired a special cook to prepare her meals; he went from stall to stall in the market to secure delicacies she enjoyed. He even had Dr. Perkins' coal grate removed and a wood-burning fireplace installed, so Grace might be warmer.

Daniel remained at her side, day after day, trying not to give up hope. But as she grew weaker and her voice fainter, he feared the worst.

When she died in his arms, Daniel burst into uncontrollable sobs. He was heartbroken.

The funeral was held in Boston on a cold, windy day.

Daniel, hand-in-hand with Fletcher and little Julia, walked behind the hearse the long distance to St. Paul's Church. He had refused to ride in a carriage, despite his heavy cold.

"No," he said. "My children and I must follow their mother to the grave on foot. I could swim to Charlestown!"

None of his friends had ever seen him so moved. He was excessively pale. Long after his friends left him in the evening, long before anyone else was up in the morning, Daniel wandered about, desolate. Now his wife lay with little Grace and baby Charles, her eldest and youngest children. He was alone.

Yet it was imperative that he take his seat in Washington. His first session as a Senator was an unhappy period for the bereaved lawyer. By April, 1829, he had packed all his books in trunks, and was determined not to return to Washington unless Zeke was sent to Congress, too. If he could have Zeke with him, he might manage. But Daniel could not face another lonely three months. Only if he could be near Zeke and his family would he return to the capital.

He soon left for Boston, where he found his sister-in-law and Zeke's oldest daughter at his home. They expected Zeke to arrive from New Hampshire in a day or two. Meanwhile, Daniel knew he must decide what was best for his children.

At three o'clock one morning Daniel was awakened by a messenger. His brother Zeke was dead! He had died suddenly in Concord. Zeke was gone. It could not be!

Even after Zeke's son-in-law, Professor Sanborn, told him the details, Daniel still could not believe it.

"Mr. Ezekiel Webster was speaking, standing erect, on a plain floor. The house was full, and the court, the jurors and the auditors intently listening to his words with their eyes fastened upon him," Professor Sanborn of Dartmouth told him. "Speaking with full force, and perfect utterance, he arrived at the end of one branch of his argument. He closed that branch, uttered the last sentence, and the last word of that sentence, with perfect tone and emphasis; and then, in an instant, erect, and his arms depending at his side, he fell backward, without bending a joint, and, so far as appeared, was dead before his head reached the floor."

"He has been my reliance throughout all my life," Daniel said to himself. "What shall I do now? Where can I turn?"

The night after the funeral Daniel gave way entirely. He wept all through the night. The shock of Zeke's death, so soon after Grace's, was more than he could bear.

"Elms Farm" was now Daniel's. But nothing in the world seemed cheerful to him, although he was well and his children were also well. Fletcher was to enter Harvard College in August; Julia and Edward were living with relatives and friends.

Often, during those days, Daniel compared Julia with Tullia, Cicero's adored daughter.

"How affectionate, how modest, how clever—the express image of my face, my speech, my very soul," Cicero had said of her, when Tullia was Julia's age.

Daniel accepted legal cases to keep his mind occupied and to earn a larger income. In the autumn he went to New York on professional business and soon found himself caught up in the most exclusive circles of social life. He might as well go out to dinner, he decided, as sit alone, unable to eat. He enjoyed small dinner parties. To his own surprise, he found that he was especially enjoying dinner parties at the home of the LeRoys.

The LeRoys were a well-known family of New York. Herman LeRoy, the father of the family, was a wealthy merchant who had been Dutch consul in New York. His second daughter, Caroline, was in her early thirties at this time and unmarried. She was a handsome, exquisitely dressed young woman, skillful in all the social graces. From the first meeting she had been attracted by the famous Daniel Webster.

Daniel, for his part, found Caroline LeRoy very agreeable. He began to consider her as a suitable mother for his children. Her youth and vivacity and strength were additional recommendations. Daniel actually found himself growing very fond of her.

In December they were married in the parlor of the Eastern Hotel, near the Battery in New York City. Daniel wrote his children, relatives, and friends of the event after it had taken place. Then, after staying a week in New York, Daniel took Caroline to Boston to meet his children.

It was scarcely two years since their mother had died. His sensitive children felt shy and strange before the fashionable young woman. But Caroline, with her affectionate nature, soon won Julia's love. With the boys it was not so easy; but eventually both Fletcher and Edward grew fond of the new Mrs. Webster. When Daniel and Caroline returned to Washington, they took Julia with them.

The election of General Jackson had been a disappointment to Daniel, and he did not look forward to the General's administration. Still, he felt it imperative to be in Washington, ready to defend the unity of the country if the tension between states continued.

That autumn, South Carolina had adopted what she called an "Exposition and Protest," which Daniel considered an example of nullification—or the failure of a state to defend federal laws within its borders. Daniel believed that such an attitude was not in keeping with the principles of the Constitution. He thought deeply about this subject, and when Congress met in December, he was prepared for the bitter controversy that would soon arise.

CHAPTER THIRTEEN

"LIBERTY AND UNION"

CAROLINE WAS TO REMEMBER THEIR FIRST EVENING in Washington. After Julia had gone to sleep, Caroline rejoined her husband in his study for tea.

"Dear Caroline, I never have women in my study," her husband greeted her with firmness. "You must have your tea in the parlor. I am occupied."

"Alone in the parlor, Daniel? I have never drunk tea alone," she said in disappointment.

Daniel took her arm gently and led her into the parlor.

"Sit here, my dear," he said. "I can see you are tired from the journey. I will gladly drink one cup of tea with you before I go back to work." He smiled as Charles brought in the tea tray.

While Caroline poured, Daniel explained the issues that troubled him.

"You see, my dear, the work in Washington is heavy

and confining. Our country is passing through a crisis."

He sipped his tea slowly, then burst out:

"What sort of a man do we have for President? Do you know that not so long ago some admirers sent him an immense cheese that weighed about twelve hundred pounds? President Jackson had it put on sawhorses in the East Room and declared open house. I looked in, quite by chance, and was astonished to find the rugs slippery from fallen particles of cheese and crackers. The room was crowded with jovial hangers-on, each with a huge chunk of cheese and a glass filled from one of the many heavily stocked liquor cabinets."

"Of course, there were only men there," Caroline observed.

"To be sure, my dear! Animals never conduct themselves with such a lack of decorum!"

"I am sure, Daniel, that the parties where ladies are present are different. Ladies have an elevating and refining effect on men."

Daniel peered at his young wife, his eyes twinkling with amusement. She was a perfect lady, such a lady as could command respect in the highest society. That was where she belonged. He must not fail her. She must one day be the First Lady!

"In a few weeks every lady in Washington will be at your door, my dear. You'll have no chance to be alone. Every evening you will find yourself at one social gathering or another, or be entertaining here."

He rose and smiled down at his wife.

"What a treasure you are, my dear," he said. "But as much as I want to put my work aside to be with you, I cannot tonight."

As he walked back to his study, Caroline looked about the room, deciding this was no place to entertain. She must speak to Daniel about getting a large

and suitable house. Meanwhile she might as well retire, as twelve-year-old Julia had already done.

Caroline had hoped friends would drop in, but
Daniel had forgotten to notify them of his arrival in
the capital. His every thought was given to his legal
cases before the Supreme Court, and to the issue of
nullification.

Daniel was absorbed in a case before the Supreme
Court, when the Senate debate over the resolution—
presented by Mr. Foote of Connecticut who suggested
the sale of public lands be limited—was brought forward. Thomas H. Benton had risen and delivered a
great speech, in which he attacked the Eastern states.
Robert Y. Hayne, an eloquent man with a musical
voice, enlarged on Senator Benton's attack.

Daniel rose to the defense of the Eastern states:
"The East! The obnoxious, the rebuked, the always-
reproached East . . . I deny the East has at any time
shown an illiberal policy toward the West . . . I pro-
nounce the whole accusation to be without the least
foundation . . . I deny it in general and I deny it in
all its particulars. I deny the sum total and I deny the
details . . ." Vigorously he took up each issue and
demolished his opponents.

There was great excitement when everyone heard
that Daniel Webster had defended the East. Why had
Daniel passed over Mr. Benton and answered Robert
Hayne?

It was expected that Hayne would reply the next
day. The Senate chamber was packed. While Senator
Benton spoke, Daniel slipped out of the Senate chamber to obtain a postponement of his legal case.

He had scarcely returned when Hayne rose and
stood before the chamber, a half-smile on his mouth,
his eyes aglow. He spoke fluently and warmly, attack-

ing not only what Mr. Webster had done but also what Daniel had said; he charged Daniel with contrasting the weakness of the slave states with the superior strength of the free states. Then Hayne denied that slavery was in any way injurious to the individual or the national character. He spoke for hours, finally going into the South Carolina doctrine of nullification. It was a good, old-fashioned doctrine, he insisted.

When Robert Hayne finished speaking, Daniel obtained the floor for the following day.

That February morning of 1830 the Senate chamber was even more crowded. Everyone felt that a great issue was at stake.

Daniel was as cool and unconcerned as he had been on the previous evening in his own home, when he had told his old friend, Judge Story, to feel no uneasiness over his encounter with Hayne, adding: "I will grind him as fine as a pinch of snuff."

The corridors were blocked. The Speaker of the House remained in his chair, but most of the members crowded into the massed Senate chamber. Ladies had been admitted, Caroline among them.

Daniel Webster made, on that occasion, a speech comparable with the greatest speeches of all time. As Caroline's eyes swept over the entranced audience, her heart swelled with pride. Hour after hour Daniel continued to demolish Robert Hayne of South Carolina. And in defending his own home state, Daniel said:

"Mr. President, I shall enter on no encomium upon Massachusetts; she needs none. There she stands. Behold her and judge for yourself. There is her history; the world knows it by heart. The past, at least, is secure. There is Boston and Concord and Lexington and Bunker Hill; and there they will remain forever.

The bones of her sons, falling in the great struggle for independence, now lie mingled with the soil of every State from New England to Georgia; and there they will lie forever . . ."

At last he came to the end of the stirring speech; his audience was breathless with excitement. His voice was cool and firm, as if he were expounding an accepted truth, as if he were clarifying the meaning of the Constitution.

"While the Union lasts we have high, exciting, gratifying prospects spread out before us, for us and our children. Beyond that I seek not to penetrate the veil. God grant that in my day, at least, that curtain may not rise! God grant that on my vision never may be opened what lies behind! When my eyes shall be turned to behold for the last time the sun in heaven, may I not see it shining on the broken and dishonored fragments of a once glorious union; on States dissevered, discordant, belligerent; on a land rent with civil feuds, or drenched, it may be, in fraternal blood. Let their last feeble and lingering glance rather behold the gorgeous ensign of the republic, now known and honored throughout the earth, still full high advanced, its arms and trophies streaming in their original lustre, not a stripe erased or polluted, not a single star obscured, bearing for its motto no such miserable interrogatory as 'What is all this worth?' nor those other words of delusion and folly, 'Liberty first and Union afterwards'; but everywhere, spread all over in characters of living light, blazing on all its ample folds, as they float over the sea and over the land, and in every wind under the whole heavens, that other sentiment, dear to every true American heart—Liberty and Union, now and forever, one and inseparable!"

When Daniel finished speaking, Robert Hayne, who

had been taking notes, arose to reply, and addressed the Senate for a short time on the Constitutional question.

Then Daniel rose again. He alluded to the vain attempt of his opponent "to reconstruct his shattered argument." Then he proceeded to set forth clearly and accurately his opponent's position. Then, step by step, he refuted it, grinding it, as he had promised his friend, "as fine as a pinch of snuff."

During the weeks of receptions and dinners which followed, no one but Daniel himself knew how often he thought of his brother, Zeke. How he regretted that Zeke could not have heard him. How often he recalled his beloved Grace's unfulfilled desire to hear him speak in the Senate. His heart ached for her and for his brother, as he stood in the midst of the gay throngs in Washington, Philadelphia, Boston and New York.

CHAPTER FOURTEEN

"MURDER WILL OUT"

SOME TWO MONTHS LATER, IN THE TOWN OF SALEM, Massachusetts, Mr. Joseph White, one of the wealthiest and most respectable citizens, was found murdered in his bed.

Mr. White, a retired merchant who was eighty-two, had no known enemies. The motive, too, was obscure. It could not have been robbery, as a large amount of money was found in his room untouched.

Meetings were called; a Vigilance Committee was formed; and every effort was made to find the murderer. But no clues could be found.

Then, suddenly, a prisoner in the New Bedford jail —seventy miles from Salem—claimed to have knowledge of the murder.

The Attorney General summoned the prisoner, whose name was Hatch, and brought him before the Grand Jury. On the testimony of the prisoner, an indictment for murder was handed down against a man

by the name of Crowninshield. Hatch testified that
Richard Crowninshield and his brother George were
the guilty men. Richard Crowninshield lived in Danvers, a town near Salem.

About a fortnight later, a strange thing happened:
Captain Joseph J. Knapp of Salem, a shipmaster and
merchant, received a letter from a man he did not
know. The letter had been mailed in Belfast, Maine,
and was signed "Charles Grant, Jr." Mr. Grant seemed
to be fully informed as to the hidden facts of old Mr.
White's murder! He insinuated that Captain Knapp
knew more than he was telling and threatened to ex-
pose the Captain if he didn't receive money by return
mail.

Thus blackmail was added to murder within a month
of the victim's death.

Captain Knapp was puzzled. He knew the murderers were in jail. Perhaps this Grant was unbalanced.
First he thought he'd answer the strange letter; then
he decided to consult someone else before he did this.
He showed the letter to his son, N. P. Knapp, a well-
known Salem lawyer, who advised his father to ignore
it.

Captain Knapp was not satisfied; he decided to consult his other sons, John Francis and Joseph J. Knapp,
who lived in Wenham, some five miles from Salem.

Mrs. Joseph J. Knapp was the daughter of old Mr.
White's niece, who had been his housekeeper until his
death.

When Joseph saw Grant's letter he said, "What a
devilish lot of trash! You'd better hand this over to the
Vigilance Committee."

By this time Captain Knapp was bored with the
whole affair of the mysterious letter. He could see no
sense in it, and doubted if the Vigilance Committee

could either. But he followed Joseph's advice, never-theless, and handed it over to them.

No sooner did the Vigilance Committee see Grant's letter than they hurriedly sent a messenger to Belfast, Maine, to find the writer.

Meanwhile, it was reported that the Knapp brothers had been attacked by highway robbers on their way from Salem to Wenham. This bold attempt in the quiet community revived the excitement of the murder. Wild tales flew about until the citizens of Salem scarcely dared to go out after dark.

In Maine it was discovered that the writer of the letter was not a man named Grant but one named Palmer, who had served a term in the state prison. He was friendly with the Crowninshields, and during a period of the previous winter he had been hidden in their house in Danvers.

Palmer claimed that a short time before the murder of old Mr. White, he had seen Frank Knapp and a man named Allen ride up to the house; and when they left, the Crowninshields had gone with them.

Later, after the Crowninshield brothers returned home, he had heard George tell Richard that Frank Knapp wanted them to kill old Mr. White. He further had said that Joseph J. Knapp had offered to pay one thousand dollars for the job. They discovered that Palmer had overheard them and offered him a cut if he would come in. He had refused, as he thought it too risky.

On the testimony of Palmer, a warrant was issued for the arrest of the Knapp brothers, who were held in custody awaiting a further investigation.

On the third day of their confinement, Joseph Knapp made a full confession. He said he had learned that his wife was to be cut off by old Mr. White and that a new will left his nephew, Stephen White, the heir. He thought if he could steal the new will, and if the old man died before his theft was discovered, his wife would have a large sum of money coming to her. He said he had talked it over with his brother Frank, who offered to find a killer for him. Frank thought he knew just the man if Joseph would pay a thousand dollars. Joseph had agreed. Frank reported that Richard Crowninshield had also agreed, so only the date remained to be decided upon.

In this coldblooded manner, two sons of a respectable and well-known family set about their evil deeds.

Joseph left a window open for the entry of Richard Crowninshield, who crept to the chamber of the old man and bludgeoned him on the head, then stabbed him a dozen or more times. Earlier in the day Joseph had obtained possession of what he believed to be the offending will, and returned to his home in Wenham.

Knapp's confession had been obtained by the Attorney General under a promise of immunity.

When Richard Crowninshield, who was in prison, heard of Joseph Knapp's confession, he committed suicide. This caused almost as much excitement as the murder itself.

When Joseph Knapp learned of Crowninshield's suicide, he repudiated his confession.

The Knapp brothers were morally as guilty of murder as it was possible to be. But, according to the Massachusetts law of the time, no accessory could be convicted of murder unless the principal had already been convicted. In this case, the man who committed the murder, that is the principal, was dead.

Therefore, the brothers would escape unless one of them could be convicted as a principal and the other as an accessory.

Frank Knapp was, therefore, tried as principal, and the Attorney General urged Daniel Webster to prosecute the case. The Knapps had secured skillful lawyers to defend them, and the Attorney General feared that these brothers, who were morally responsible for the killing, might escape.

Daniel declined. He had never taken this sort of case and he disliked the idea. Even when Judge Story, who was a relative of the murdered man, urged him to consider it, Daniel remained undecided.

Ultimately he was won over by a sense of duty. At the trial of Frank Knapp he made such a speech to the jury that a conviction was practically assured. Among other things he said:

"An aged man, without an enemy in the world, in his own house and in his own bed, is made the victim of a butcherly murder for mere pay . . . Deep sleep had fallen upon the destined victim and all beneath his roof. A healthful old man to whom sleep was sweet, the first sound slumbers of the night held him in their soft but strong embrace.

"The assassin enters through the window already prepared . . . The face of the innocent sleeper is turned from the murderer, and the beams of the moon, resting on the gray locks of his aged temple, show him where to strike . . .

"The deed is done. He retreats, retraces his steps to the window, passes out through it as he came in, and escapes. He had done the murder . . . No eye had seen him. No ear had heard him. The secret is his own and it is safe.

"Ah, gentlemen, that was a dreadful mistake. Such a secret can be safe nowhere. The whole creation of God has neither nook nor corner where the guilty man can bestow it and say it is safe. Not to speak of the eye which pierces through all disguises, and beholds everything as in the splendor of noon, such secrets of guilt are never safe from detection, even by men.

"True it is, generally speaking, that 'Murder will out!'"

Frank Knapp was hanged. Later, Joseph Knapp was also found guilty and hanged.

Fletcher Webster had followed the trial with intense interest. One evening he and his father spoke of it.

"Do you know, Fletcher," Daniel asked, "that if Joseph Knapp had gone on the stand and testified, instead of refusing to do so, and if his story had been believed by the jury, it might have freed his brother, as well as himself?"

"It seems especially wrong to kill such a helpless old man," said Fletcher. "It's sordid, too, to take life for money. They must be evil men. It is fortunate they were not clever, or they might never have been caught."

"Had they been the cleverest young men in the world, Fletcher, they would have been caught," Daniel Webster assured his son. "Murder will out!"

A BLACK CLOUD GATHERS

As a lawyer, as a statesman, as an orator, Daniel Webster was now preeminent in his own country and, many thought, in the world. Men never tired of comparing him with the Greek Demosthenes, the Romans Livy, Cato, and Cicero.

Yet all this adulation did not go to Daniel's head. Strangely, too, he never became a politician; in politics he was innocent of guile. He spoke as he believed; he cooperated with any man of similar ideas, no matter what party the man was in.

When Daniel saw that John C. Calhoun was uniting the men of the South in a secession party, he censured his old friend. To Daniel, it seemed un-American for men to unite for any purpose other than to uphold the Constitution and the liberties of the people.

With the first issue of the *Liberator*, William Lloyd Garrison insisted:

"I will be as harsh as truth, and as uncompromising

115

as justice. On this subject, I do not wish to think, or speak, or write, with moderation. No! No! Tell a man whose house is on fire to give a moderate alarm . . . tell the mother to gradually extricate her babe from the fire into which it has fallen—urge me not to use moderation in a cause like the present. I am in earnest —I will not equivocate—I will not excuse—I WILL BE HEARD."

Soon the State of Georgia was so incensed that it offered five thousand dollars to anyone who would kidnap Mr. Garrison and bring him to the southern state. Anti-slavery riots took place in New York and Philadelphia. The year of the Whig convention, Garrison went to Boston.

Julia came rushing in one day, her hair flying, her dark eyes bright with excitement.

"Mother! Father!" she called. "There are crowds on the streets. I heard men say they are mobbing Mr. Garrison."

"I'm thankful you are safe in the house, my dear," said Caroline. "I should have sent to school for you had I known. The violent speeches must have aroused the people of Boston. Mr. Garrison is a menace."

"But, Mother, they're dragging him through the streets! They want to kill him! I know they do! They were acting like crazy people."

"Well, that's not to be wondered at, Julia," Daniel said, striding around the room. "Mobs are made up of crazy people. People who permit their emotions to rule their intelligence commit the greatest follies in the world. However, I trust no real harm comes to Mr. Garrison. It would not speak well for Boston. Nor do I personally desire any harm even to those enemies of the Constitution."

He paused and looked solemnly at his wife and daughter.

"Many are saying there is something higher than the Constitution and, of course, there is: God. But who are they to set themselves up as the sole interpreters of God's will?"

The next year another abolitionist, George G. Birney, was mobbed in Cincinnati. In various parts of the country, houses were burned, the occupants tarred and feathered. In Illinois, a minister who published an abolitionist paper was killed by the mob and his press was destroyed. All over the country, people were aroused.

John C. Calhoun tried to get a law passed that would forbid the use of the mails for anti-slavery books, newspapers, tracts and pictures.

That year New York City gave Daniel Webster a great public welcome and he addressed an immense crowd at Niblo's Garden. Speaking on the value of the Constitution, he said:

"Under the present Constitution, wisely administered, all are safe, happy and renowned . . . But if its system is broken, its fragments must fall alike on all."

He spoke in favor of freedom of speech:

"On the general question of slavery, a great portion of the community is already excited . . . It has arrested the religious feeling of the country; it has taken hold on the consciences of men. He is a rash man, indeed, and little conversant with human nature, and especially has he a very erroneous estimate of the character of the people of this country, who supposes that a feeling of this kind is to be trifled with or despised . . .

"But to coerce it into silence, to endeavor to restrain its free expression . . . I know nothing, even the Constitution or the Union itself, which would not be endangered by the explosion which might follow."

He ended, as always, with a clarion call for Union and Liberty:

"Let us, then, stand by the Constitution, as it is, and by our country, as it is—one, united and entire; let it be a truth engraven on our hearts, let it be borne on the flag under which we rally in every exigency, that we have ONE COUNTRY, ONE CONSTITUTION, ONE DESTINY."

From New York Daniel hastened to his beloved Marshfield. Nearby there was a smaller house which he called Careswell. It was prepared for his son's future use, when Fletcher should have a family. Daniel loved his children and was constantly planning for them.

Daniel always went fishing the first day with Seth Peterson. This time they had a long day at sea and caught a fine halibut, as well as many smaller fish.

"It's time we were getting home, Mr. Webster." Seth looked at the gathering fog and frowned.

"Just let me have another half hour," urged Daniel.

As the darkness increased, Seth became more and more uneasy. "We must go, Mr. Webster," he said.

So they turned the boat toward home.

"Look out, Seth!" called Daniel. "You'll hit a sunken rock!"

Seth was looking for the river, determined to run in. It was so dark Daniel stood upright in the boat and tried to peer ahead.

This cut off Seth's view. Yet he didn't like to ask Mr. Webster to sit down. Still it was a dangerous position.

At last he said: "Mr. Webster, you're a dreadful bad lantern!"

Quick as a shot Daniel sat down in the boat; he was still anxious, but he said not another word.

Finally, Seth steered the boat safely in. And as Daniel felt the sturdy boards of the dock beneath his feet, he let out a great shout. He shouted and sang at the top of his voice all the way back to the house.

The next night he went, as he so often did, into Mrs. Baker's comfortable room. His housekeeper was an old friend, and he enjoyed sitting before her great fireplace and talking with her. He put some potatoes in the ashes and when they were ready, he called:

"Bring out some of that cold turkey, Mrs. Baker. Supper is ready!"

Later his farm hands joined him and together they discussed various problems and made plans for future work.

The next day Caroline and the children arrived with a group of friends. Everyone around Marshfield called Daniel "Squire," and he was much amused by it.

He was particularly happy that his good friend, Peter Harvey, had come to visit. That evening, while the ladies played whist, the men sat in his library and talked.

When they were preparing to join the other guests, Daniel stopped and took a handsome volume from his bookshelves.

"My dear Harvey, you must see my prize goose!"

Daniel turned the leaves of Audubon's *Birds of America* until he came to the picture of a beautiful Canada goose. The young artist had drawn it by the shore of Daniel's little lake.

"Audubon took more than two days to get that bird

the way he wanted it, but it was worth the time, wasn't it, Harvey?" Daniel's eyes shone with admiration.

"I believe you told me," Mr. Harvey said, "that you presented the young artist with a cartload of miscellaneous birds, which you had ordered all the hunters around here to kill for you."

"That's true," Daniel admitted. "But it was for a scientific and artistic purpose, Harvey. Not just for the sake of killing. I haven't liked to shoot a bird since I was a boy."

Returning the book carefully to the shelves, Daniel continued: "Audubon studied the attitude of that Canada goose for a whole day and spent three days getting the portrait."

He sighed in admiration of the artist, as he led his guest into the larger sitting room to join in the evening game of whist.

When winter came, the Websters went again to Washington. Daniel's efforts to resign from the Senate and return to private practice had met with so much resistance that he decided to continue.

In January he replied to Mr. Calhoun, whom Daniel believed was trying to make a new Constitution.

The Senate was crowded to capacity when Daniel charged John C. Calhoun of knowingly and willfully attempting to break up the Union. He said:

"Mr. Calhoun now states he will march off under the banner of States' Rights. March off from Where? March off from What? We have been contending for great principles. We have been struggling to maintain liberty . . . under the old flag, the true American flag . . . He now, however, tells us he marches off under a States' Rights Banner . . .

"Let him go. I remain. I am where I have ever been and ever mean to be. Here, standing on the platform of the general Constitution, a platform broad enough and firm enough to uphold the interest of the whole country . . . I move off under no banner not known to the whole American people, and to their Constitution and their laws."

A few days later he spoke again to Caroline about going to England.

"Even though I assumed my Senate duties for another six years, there seems no valid reason why we cannot go to England for the six months' recess," he said.

"I should enjoy it immensely," Caroline replied happily.

"Julia must come with us," said Daniel. "I can make no plans which do not include my beloved Julia."

"But what about her marriage?" Caroline asked. "Will young Samuel Appleton be willing to wait for our return?"

"I would not ask that. He can join us, and they can be married in London." Daniel's eyes sparkled. "That will be just the thing. He was born in England and had his early education there. I think I shall engage passage for May. I am sure our dear friend, Harriette Paige, will join us, and Edward can follow later when his Dartmouth classes are over for this year. Perhaps he and Samuel Appleton can come over together. I dislike leaving Fletcher. I wish he might come, too . . ."

"You know he can't just now, Daniel; nor would he probably wish to, with Baby Grace only eighteen months old. Caroline would not consent, I feel sure, to take such a young child across the ocean."

"No, of course you are right, Caroline," Daniel said.

"Still I like my family all together, and our new daughter Caroline is a charming young woman. She would add to our party."

"Indeed she would," Caroline agreed, "but they have plenty of time to travel."

"I shall be going entirely in a private capacity, you know, but I have many friends in England whom I have long promised to visit. So I feel sure we'll have a very pleasant trip."

"Indeed we shall," Caroline eagerly agreed. "I hope we can be presented at Court. Young Victoria must be charming. Think of being Queen of England and still in your 'teens!"

"We'll give the whole matter our serious consideration," Daniel smiled. "I can see no reason at present why we should not go."

"THE NOTABLEST OF NOTABLES"

IN MAY, DANIEL WEBSTER SAILED WITH HIS WIFE, HIS daughter, and Mrs. William Paige. The Atlantic crossing was so fast that it amazed everyone on board; it took only fifteen days! Caroline was seasick during the entire trip, but young Julia and her father enjoyed every minute of it.

This holiday was to be the last period of complete happiness Daniel Webster would know. Ahead lay strife and bitterness, sorrow beyond belief, as he climbed the steep and jagged road to enduring fame.

But he arrived in Liverpool carefree and happy, anxious to view the English country and the fine cattle of which he had often heard. Their first stop was at the old city of Chester; as they proceeded through the Shakespeare country, they stopped again and again to examine fine cattle and view luxuriant gardens. When they reached London, they stayed in the fashionable Brunswick Hotel in Hanover Square.

123

Daniel was fifty-seven and full of vitality. His enthusiasm delighted everyone he met. But he was happiest with Julia, and watched with admiration as she rode off toward Richmond Hill.

Julia's horsemanship was the delight of her English escorts. And Daniel smiled to himself as he remembered how she gaily rode around Marshfield and the New Hampshire country. Neither of her brothers dared try some of the spirited mounts she so easily rode. Daniel remembered how her thick, beautiful hair would fly in the wind as she raced around the Green Harbor roads, jumped the fences, and returned with rosy cheeks and shining dark eyes. Now, in London, how demure she looked in her proper riding costume, sitting so firmly on her side-saddle as she started off on a canter in Rotten Row. What energy, what spirit that demureness concealed, Daniel thought—for it was his own, his gift to his beloved daughter.

Caroline was immediately at home with the social set of London. Persons with high titles called and asked them to dinner or for week ends. Even the newspapers publicly welcomed them! He laughingly said it was a wonder their heads weren't turned by all this abounding kindness.

They all four had breakfast with Charles Dickens, then a young man just tasting fame. The ladies of the party were very excited. The talk was of Mr. Pickwick that morning.

At other breakfasts they met many notables, including the poets, Samuel Taylor Coleridge, William Wordsworth, and Tom Moore. Daniel was enchanted with Wordsworth's description of the Lake country.

"I think these English breakfasts are the most delightful, informal gatherings in the world," Daniel said one morning. "But as they begin around ten and last until after twelve, they can be enjoyed only by persons with entire leisure."

"The odd thing here is, Father, that no one seems to work," laughed Julia.

"Perhaps they have put their work aside to meet a famous man," suggested Caroline, looking with admiration at her handsome husband.

"Perhaps so, but even the young men never seem to be occupied," Julia frowned. "I'm glad Samuel didn't stay over here. I like him better for being an American and working at his profession."

"Then you won't want to be presented to the Queen tonight as we have planned," Daniel turned to his radiant daughter with a twinkle in his eyes.

"Don't be silly!" Julia sprang from her chair and threw her arms around his neck. "You know I've always said I'd go even into a lion's den to be with you!"

"I doubt you will find Buckingham Palace a lion's den," Caroline said. She had been distressed by the light attitude her husband assumed toward this important meeting with Queen Victoria.

Caroline had shopped constantly, and had bought a gown far more expensive than she intended. Then she'd purchased all the necessary accessories, borrowing a scarf for her hair and a fan. Everything must be precisely correct for this evening of evenings, she felt.

As they assembled to await the carriage, Daniel was impressed by the easy, almost regal bearing of his slender wife. Harriette Paige looked beautiful, as always. But it was Julia who took his breath away. She was the loveliest thing he had ever seen, he thought, like a princess in a fairy tale.

After the great moment had come and gone, Caroline almost agreed with her husband that the event was scarcely worth the frantic preparation. For two hours or more they all waited in a small side-room. When the time for the bow arrived, it was brief. The young Queen was charming, but far less lovely and far less bright than Julia, as Daniel had said.

If Daniel was often bored with his wife's social aspirations in London, he was able to enjoy his own kind of time in Oxford.

Daniel with his three lady companions went there the middle of July.

Here he addressed some twenty-five hundred members of an agricultural society, and it was the only public speech he made during his entire visit in England.

The party stayed at the Angel Hotel in Oxford. John Kenyon, a good friend of George Ticknor's, joined them; and while Daniel went to make his address, Mr. Kenyon dined at the hotel with the ladies.

Early in the evening Daniel returned. He slipped gaily into the room where the others were chatting, and even danced a few steps. His dark eyes were twinkling.

"I like your English farmers. They are fine upstanding men, my sort of men," Daniel said courteously.

"I wish I might have heard your speech," returned Kenyon.

"If you mean that seriously . . ." Daniel turned to the ladies and met three expectant pairs of eyes. "I'll repeat it here. It's short."

Whereupon he started off, without any notes:

"The noble chairman was pleased to speak of the people of the United States as kindred in blood with the people of England. I am an American. I was born on that great continent, and am wedded to the fortunes of my country, for well or for woe. There is no other region of the earth which I can call my country.

But I know, and am proud to know, what blood flows in these veins.

"I am happy to stand here today and to remember that although my ancestors for several generations lie buried beneath the soil of the western continent, yet there has been a time when my ancestors toiled in the same cities and villages, cultivated adjacent fields, and worked together to build up that great structure of civil polity which has made England what England is.

"When I was about to embark for this country some friends asked me what I was going to England for. To be sure, gentlemen, I came for no object of business, public or private; but I told them I was coming to see relations, my kith and kin of the old Saxon race . . ."

Mr. Kenyon was charmed; he realized that a sense of modesty had prevented Mr. Webster from making a pretentious speech.

"Mr. Webster," he blurted out, "I don't think political power should be in the hands of the great land owners and the rich businessmen; I've come to think it should be in the hands of the laboring man."

Daniel rose and good-naturedly put his hands on John Kenyon's shoulders.

"Don't talk so," Daniel said soberly. "Depend on it, if you put the property in one set of hands and the political power in another, the power won't rest till it has got hold of the property."

Daniel then launched into a discussion of recent English history which astonished his guest in its abundance of knowledge. He had surprised other Englishmen by his familiarity with every monument in Westminister Abbey. His knowledge of various breeds of cattle, their owners and breeders, amazed even his acquaintances of the agricultural society.

Daniel was enchanted with Oxford. He delighted

in the medieval architecture of the buildings. As he walked down High Street with his three lady companions, he pointed out the seventeenth-century gateways of University College. Here, in the larger quadrangle, he had spoken on the previous night. Then they turned down Logic Lane to Merton College, which was one of the oldest of the colleges.

"At first, Caroline," Daniel instructed his wife, "the scholars here were known as 'postmasters.'"

"How very odd!" exclaimed his wife.

"Not as odd as you may think, my dear," retorted Daniel gaily. "It probably comes from the Latin *portionista*. But it's the buildings we've come to see. This gateway tower dates from the first years of the fifteenth century."

They soon found themselves in the chapel, with its beautiful choir windows of thirteenth-century glass. Julia could hardly tear herself away from the marvelous colors. She had never seen anything more exquisite.

"You go to other places you want to see, but leave me here," she implored.

So while Julia and Harriette stayed to admire the chapel, Daniel led Caroline to the thirteenth-century muniments room, or treasury. His wife was amazed at how well he found his way about, quite as if he had known the university town from boyhood.

"That lofty stone roof is a marvel," he observed, as they went into the picturesque Mob Quadrangle. "It's the oldest part of the college.

"Famous men have studied here—philosophers and metaphysicians," he went on in a sober voice. "Duns Scotus, William of Ockham, and the great Wycliffe."

As he spoke, Julia and Harriette joined them.

"Isn't it marvelous, Father?" Julia asked softly. "I'm too happy!"

Now Daniel led his party down Merton Street, past the college gardens, and up King to High Street. Ahead lay Magdalen Tower and the old bridge over the Cherwell.

"Why, this is the most beautiful college of all!" Julia exclaimed with delight. "I want to climb that tower for the view!"

By the time they returned to the hotel, it was almost the dinner hour. Caroline was completely exhausted and begged to be excused. So Daniel ate with the younger ladies and discussed the sights they would see the next day.

"Duke Humphrey's library at the Bodleian, and the Christ Church meadow are as fine as anything I've seen," he said. "We'll take a carriage tomorrow and drive all about the town. I should like to go up some of the hills hereabouts and see Oxford from various sides."

"That would be wonderful," Julia agreed. "Then on we go to Eton and Windsor!"

Between Oxford and Windsor, the party stopped to visit Miss Mitford, whose stories, "Our Village," had increased her popularity as an author. She was about fifty, a small, plump, old-fashioned woman who delighted Daniel.

They walked in her garden and talked endlessly about flowers and shrubs.

"The primrose and the cowslip, immortalized by Shakespeare and Milton, the sweet-scented violets, both white and purple, and the little wild pansy renowned as the love-in-idleness of Shakespeare's famous compliment to Queen Elizabeth, I have already sent to America to a friend," Miss Mitford told Daniel.

"Have you no interest in any of our flowers?" he asked.

"From the vivid descriptions by Miss Martineau, I have become somewhat interested in two—the scarlet lily of New York and of the Canada woods and the fringed gentian of Niagara," she admitted.

Daniel turned to Julia, who was walking arm-in-arm with Caroline.

"Remember to send Miss Mitford seeds of the scarlet lily and fringed gentian," he whispered. Julia nodded understandingly.

From Windsor they went through the lake region to Scotland. The trip was tiring and Daniel resented the constant hurrying from one place to another. They had paused briefly to visit Lord Lowther at his magnificent castle. The view from the terrace, over hills and lakes, was impressive; but Daniel preferred Marshfield and the sea.

One day, as they sat talking, Daniel complained, "We have no time to see anything as it ought to be seen. If I could have gone through this lake region at leisure, and with one friend of discernment, taste and feeling, I should have experienced, I am sure, the greatest possible delight."

"It would take years and years, Daniel, to travel slowly as you prefer to do," Caroline retorted. "However could we see everything, even if we lingered everywhere?"

"Oh, Caroline, don't tell me you are like the rest of these crowds who rush like mad on every side of us!"

"Of course I'm not! I would have much preferred to stay in London. But I consider it my duty to see Scotland now that I'm here."

"Well, we are about to fulfill your duty for you!" Daniel jovially twisted one of his wife's curls.

"Samuel is in London!" Julia rushed in, her eyes

shining. "Edward and he came over on the *British Queen!*"

"You can see, Daniel, why we must rush through Scotland," said his wife with a smile.

> " 'O young Lochinvar is come out of the west,
>   Through all the wide border his steed was
>   the best . . .' "

quoted Daniel, his eyes twinkling. To Julia he whispered gaily, "What better steed than the *British Queen?*"

> " 'So faithful in love, so dauntless in war,
>   There never was knight like the young Lochinvar!' "

Daniel danced around the room, swinging Julia about with him. All his ill humor had been dispelled.

They all enjoyed Scotland. But as they hurried through the lake country—immortalized by Sir Walter Scott's narrative poem, "The Lady of the Lake"—Daniel thought sadly of Grace, his first wife. He had read Scott's poem to her during their happy evenings together, and every sight reminded him of her.

After a few brief weeks they were back in London, where Julia rushed around to prepare for her wedding.

This took place at the end of September in the fashionable St. George's Church in Hanover Square, near their hotel. Only the family and a few friends were present. After the ceremony the Appletons—Julia and Samuel—left for the continent. Edward soon followed; he intended to spend a year with the Edward Everetts, studying in Geneva.

One night in London, some two months later, after Caroline had gone to sleep, Daniel sat down at the small table-desk and wrote one of his most memorable verses, which he called "The Memory of the Heart."

If stores of dry and learned lore we gain,
We keep them in the memory of the brain;
Names, things and facts—whatever we knowledge call,
There is the common ledger for them all;
And images on this cold surface traced
Make slight impressions, and are soon effaced.

But we've a page more glowing and more bright,
On which our friendship and our love to write;
That these may never from the soul depart,
We trust them to *the memory of the heart*.
There is no dimming—no effacement here;
Each new pulsation keeps the record clear;
Warm, golden letters all the tablet fill
Nor lose their lustre till the heart stands still.

Daniel had been disappointed in the great Parliamentary orator, Macaulay, whom he heard speak in the House of Commons. But Thomas Carlyle, the famous author and critic, was not disappointed in Daniel Webster.

"I saw at breakfast the American Webster," Carlyle wrote a friend, "a perfectly bred man, though not English in breeding. He is a magnificent specimen. You might say to all the world 'This is our Yankee Englishman; such limbs we make in Yankee Land!' As a logic-fencer, advocate, or parliamentary Hercules, one would incline to back him at first sight against all the extant world.

"Daniel Webster is the notablest of notables!"

CHAPTER SEVENTEEN

"CANDIDATE FOR TRUTH"

DANIEL WEBSTER RETURNED FROM HIS VISIT TO ENG-
land to find the Presidential campaign in full
swing. All signs pointed to a Whig victory; so
when Daniel was entered in the Massachusetts race
for candidates, he knew his own nomination was hope-
less.

William Henry Harrison, who had been an Indian
fighter and was called "the hero of Tippecanoe," was
the chosen candidate for the picturesque campaign.
Throughout the country it was the log cabin, the coonskin on the wall, the door on the latch—welcoming all
comers. Beside the door stood the buckeye bench and
beside the bench, the barrel of cider. The log cabin was
even mounted on wheels and dragged about. Badges
were everywhere; newspapers, magazines, pamphlets
all depicted the log cabin.

It was a campaign of laughter and song. And

133

throughout the country were banners on which was enscribed:

"Farewell dear Van,
     You're not our man,
     To guide the ship,
     We'll try old Tip."

The marchers in coonskin caps shouted over and over again: "Tippecanoe and Tyler, too."

In several cities Daniel Webster made great speeches. He often traveled on one of the new trains, which resembled a stagecoach mounted on flat boards, which in turn were mounted on wheels. The trains had second stories which were open and roofed with flat awnings. Several coaches were coupled together and drawn on narrow tracks by a flat contraption on which an engine was mounted and where baggage was carried.

Daniel delighted in all new inventions, especially those which benefited his fellow men and made their lives less painful. Such a discovery was ether, which was slowly coming into general use in England and America. The Morse code was also new and terribly exciting to Daniel, who often said he lived in such an age of scientific discovery and invention as the world had never before seen.

At Saratoga he told thousands of listeners:

"Gentlemen, it did not happen to me to be born in a log cabin; but my elder brothers and sisters were born in a log cabin, raised amid the snowdrifts of New Hampshire at a period so early that when the smoke first rose from the rude chimney over the frozen hills, there was no similar evidence of a white man's habitation between it and the settlements on the rivers of Canada.

"I carry my children to it, to teach them the hardships endured by generations which have gone before them . . . If ever I am ashamed of it," Daniel went on, "or if I ever fail in affectionate veneration for him who raised it . . . and shrank from no danger or toil, no sacrifice to serve his country, to raise his children to a condition better than his own—may my name and the name of my posterity be blotted from the memory of mankind!"

Eager crowds gathered at every stopping place, the late winter and spring of 1840. At Bunker Hill there were more than seventy-five thousand. Daniel Webster was in far greater demand as a speaker than the Presidential candidate! Even in Richmond, Virginia, and in Baltimore, Maryland, huge crowds gathered to hear him.

When the election was won, President Harrison asked Henry Clay to be Secretary of State. When Clay declined, the President offered either that or the office of Secretary of the Treasury to Daniel Webster.

"I have decided to accept Harrison's offer," Daniel told Caroline one evening. "I shall take the State Department because I believe I can be of the most use to my country there."

"It's a shame, Daniel, that you are not the President," said his wife affectionately. "You are a much superior man, in every way, to President Harrison. I cannot understand why you weren't chosen the Whig candidate."

"Perhaps next time . . ." Daniel's tired eyes looked into her eager ones. No woman had ever been as ambitious for him as Caroline was. He sighed; he was very tired. It had been a strenuous campaign and he was no longer young.

"I have no real desire to enter the Cabinet, and Julia

writes that she thinks I should leave Washington and return to Marshfield to be near her and her dear children. She fears for my health if I remain in Washington."

"Do you mean Julia wants you to give up all this?" Caroline was plainly amazed at the idea.

"Oh, I have already written Julia of my intention to accept the President's offer," Daniel reassured his wife. "You shall take the finest house in Washington, if you desire, and give the finest parties and, I hope, have the finest time in the whole world!"

Daniel raised his tired body from the chair. "But now I am obliged to ask you to allow me to withdraw to my study to wrestle with the Roman proconsuls which clutter up the President's inaugural address."

He bowed graciously and kissed his wife's hand. Then he walked slowly from the sitting room.

Just one month after the inauguration, President Harrison died suddenly. It fell to the Cabinet to decide who would be appointed President, as this was the first time a President had died in office.

Fletcher Webster, Daniel's oldest son, was at this time Chief Clerk of the State Department. Daniel had him take a message to Vice-President Tyler, asking him to come at once to Washington. Daniel himself was absorbed in solicitous attentions to the widow and children of the deceased President.

Just as Daniel had feared, the question of establishing a National Bank became an issue in Congress. After the new President's veto, the Whigs tried again, only to have President Tyler veto the bill for a second time!

The quarrel between the Whigs and the President, who had been their own choice for Vice-President, was now in the open. Exactly what Daniel had dreaded had come to pass—it was a deadlock!

In anger and despair, every member of the Cabinet, except Daniel Webster, resigned.

What ought he to do? Should he follow his colleagues? Should he, too, resign?

He had entered the Cabinet to conduct the foreign affairs of his country. Lord Ashburton, whom he had met in England, was expected to arrive in Washington soon to arrange a treaty with Britain. The strained relations between Washington and London were a source of deep concern to Daniel.

The Americans several years before had aided the Canadian rebels in the insurrection of 1837. Then they called forth retaliation from the Canadian volunteers, who crossed the Niagara River and sank the *Caroline,* an American steamship that was supplying the Canadian rebels. A Canadian even boasted in a New York tavern that he had killed an American citizen during this attack!

These accusations and counter-accusations had brought the two countries to the verge of war.

A few years after this episode, the ship, *Creole,* which was transporting slaves from Virginia to New Orleans, put in at the British Bahamas after the slaves had mutinied and killed a white passenger.

The British had, quite properly, executed the murderers. Then, quite improperly, according to the opinion of many Southerners, they had set the rest of the slaves free. Having freed their own slaves more than a decade before this incident, they held this action in the Bahamas was proper.

There were many other irritations, small and great, which demanded attention. Daniel felt he was the best man available to work out these troubles in an amicable fashion.

Where did his duty lie?

All night long Daniel paced up and down, up and down.

Caroline was so disturbed by the steady footfalls, she could not sleep. Hour after hour those footsteps, so steady, so constant, so firm, increased her apprehension.

When morning came Daniel went to her room, where she was drinking tea.

"I trust I did not disturb you, Caroline," he greeted her kindly. "You see, my dear, my colleagues of the Cabinet, by acting rashly, have posed me a difficult problem. I am a moderate man, you know. I cannot throw the great foreign concerns of my country into disorder or danger by any abrupt party-proceeding."

"But if you break with the Whig party, where will you be?" Caroline's voice was indistinct with emotion as she looked into her husband's dark eyes. His face looked haggard in the early morning light. The familiar blue coat and buff waistcoat looked almost as if they had been slept in.

"If I remain alone, it will be because I do not see sufficient reason for the action of my colleagues. Even if I saw good and sufficient reason to resigning, I should not go without giving the President notice."

Caroline did not reply. She was too inwardly disturbed to speak. She knew too well that Daniel was sacrificing, by such independent action, his chance of becoming the Whig nominee for President.

"Do not let yourself be disturbed by the newspaper attacks, Caroline. Every public man is subject to such attacks on occasion," he explained, in an effort to soothe her.

"But it is your own party who is attacking you! Where will you be if the Whigs throw you out?" his wife cried, in a broken voice. "Consider what it means, Daniel! Do you not desire to attain the highest office your country has to offer?"

Daniel sat down on one of the small chairs in his wife's boudoir. He appeared utterly relaxed and serene. She couldn't understand it.

"The ends I aim at, Caroline, must be my country's, my God's, and Truth's." His eyes had a faraway look.

"I would far rather be a candidate for Truth than a candidate for the Presidency of the United States," Daniel continued quietly. "I had not thought to make such a choice, but if I must, I must."

"Why must you? Why do you see this matter in such a different light from your Whig colleagues? You know it is President Tyler who has bolted his own party, not the men in his Cabinet. Are you going to bolt with him?"

Caroline drew a pale pink covering more closely about her shoulders and shivered with nervousness.

"Perhaps we see the matter differently because I put my country before my political party, and the other men do not. But I did not come in here to excite you, Caroline," he said gently. "If you cannot understand my action, you are in good company."

He paused. Again his eyes had the faraway look. Perhaps he was seeing his father or Zeke or the home of his childhood. Caroline was momentarily touched. But before she could speak, Daniel went on:

"Apparently none of my Whig colleagues understands me any better than my wife does," he said sadly. "Never mind. Try to rest. I have endless records to study before the arrival of Alexander Baring, Lord Ashburton."

He bent to kiss her.

"You must never think, Daniel, that I do not have complete faith in your judgment," she whispered. "It is just that . . ."

"I know . . ." he replied gently. Then he hurried from the room.

Many months later, the Webster-Ashburton Treaty completed, Daniel was dining with his elder son, Fletcher. Daniel was to leave soon for Marshfield to prepare for Lord Ashburton's visit there, after which he planned to take a much needed rest.

"What do you hear of my miniature namesake and his adorable sister, Grace, and your own dear Caroline?" Daniel asked.

"My wife and children are well and looking forward to your return to Marshfield. They say Green Harbor misses you as they never miss anyone else," Fletcher replied. "By the way, Caroline says little Daniel grows more like you week by week."

"Let us toast the two Carolines, our wives," he said.

"As to you, sir, and the Treaty," his son added, "I have been enraged at the way the newspapers are attacking you. It's calumny, sir!"

"Well, the Treaty has been ratified by a vote of thirty-nine to nine, which is a larger majority than I had expected. I feel confident that when the terms are made fully public, it will be admitted I have done all any man could do for the honor of his country."

"How well I know that, sir, and so did Lord Ashburton for his; but there are carping critics on both sides of the Atlantic." Fletcher looked admiringly at his famous father.

"Lord Ashburton is a fine gentleman," Daniel agreed heartily. "A good friend and a loyal Englishman. I shall be proud to entertain him at Marshfield."

"Why did you refuse the dinner in New York? He

would have liked to have you there. It will be a gala occasion."

"It seemed to be indelicate to me, Fletcher, to take any of the attention from our guest. Had I gone, I fear I inevitably would have done so. Therefore I felt I must refuse."

"I think you are the most considerate man alive!" exclaimed his son. "You always manage to do the right thing. Why, everyone thought the Treaty would break down over the *Creole* affair, but I knew you would bring your country through!"

"It was pretty ticklish for a time, but President Tyler backed me up, and we managed to compromise. We managed to compromise everywhere, you might say. That is what a treaty is, Fletcher—a compromise to end trouble and to avoid future trouble between nations. We should never quarrel with England; they are our blood-brothers."

"But many brothers have feuds, Father!"

"True. Yet I don't want to see our country quarrel with England if I can prevent it. Why, I spent two of the longest and most difficult days of my life before I could obtain from Lord Ashburton the word 'apology,' which occurs in his letter on the *Caroline* affair!"

"I know how hard it has been, sir," Fletcher said, sympathetically. "You've worked yourself to death for your country—and look how they repay you with scurrilous attacks! I hope when Lord Ashburton leaves, you spend a month fishing—without reading one newspaper!"

"I can promise that, especially if you can find the time to accompany the Commodore and me."

"I suppose you'll insist I arise at daybreak," returned Fletcher, with a broad smile. "Charles Lanman was telling me that the last time he went to Marshfield with you, you stole into his room at the crack of dawn and aroused him from a deep sleep shouting: 'Awake, sluggard, and look upon this glorious scene, for the sky and the ocean are enveloped in flames!'"

"I must warn Charles not to tell tales out of school," Daniel said with mock severity. "I can't have my own clerk laughing at me, now can I?"

Fletcher's smile broadened. He was delighted to see his father in one of his cheerful moods.

"Have you heard lately from Edward?" he asked.

"Yes," Daniel paused and looked away. "He appears to be content with his law studies in Boston."

"I have an accomplished brother," said Fletcher with satisfaction. "He's really a wonderful mathematician. Since you left him in Geneva after your English trip and his year in Florence with Mr. Everett, he's quite a linguist, too! If I could envy such a sweet person, I'd envy him. And now he has his Dartmouth degree, and he has settled down to read law! Are you sure, Father, that Edward is happy studying law?"

"No, Fletcher, I'm far from sure about it. He's rather like I was as a young man. I couldn't decide what I wanted to do, either. Circumstances pushed me into law, you know. I often think I should have had a better life if I had been a farmer, even a poor one!"

"You know you don't mean that! I know how devoted you are to the sea and the old farm, to hunting and fishing, to all outdoor life; but you are more devoted to your country." Fletcher was serious. "Why, sir, what would your country have done without you? This famous treaty—which I heard a Senator say was the most important since the Treaty of Ghent—would never have been completed! Nor would good relations still exist between the slave-holding states and the northern free states, if you were not here to keep the peace!"

"I doubt Mr. Garrison would agree with you about the excellence of my moderation, nor would the leaders of the slave states think any the better of it!" his father said with a broad smile. "The center of the road is not a popular path, Fletcher. When you see both sides of a question, men are apt to imagine you sit on a fence!"

"But it isn't like that with you, sir!"

"No, Fletcher, it isn't. I only try to prevent narrow fanatics from tearing our Constitution into tatters. The men who are determined to tear it up, if they succeed in so doing, will live to rue the day. I am sure of it. I would defend the Constitution with my life!"

"So would I, sir!" echoed Fletcher, little realizing that in the future he was going to give his life fighting to keep his country true to her Constitution.

"When men allow their passions to rule their common sense, I fear the worst," Daniel Webster said solemnly. "They forget that they are human beings, and often become less than animals. You must never permit the voice of reason to be hushed in a conflict of the passions!"

Fletcher rose. "You know that I never shall, sir. But I am tired now—I need more sleep than you do, Father. How you keep well with only six hours a night, I can't understand. I should go to sleep on my feet!"

"Forgive me, Fletcher," Daniel said, instantly contrite. "Let me take you to your door. I can as well go home now and answer some over-due letters."

The next month three thousand people were closely packed into Faneuil Hall in Boston—cold, critical, censorious persons, for the most part. They had come to hear Daniel Webster "explain" his so-called loyalty to President Tyler and his so-called disloyalty to the

Whig party, of which he had been an outstanding member.

When he rose on the platform to acknowledge the Mayor's introduction, his strong, broad figure loomed more majestic than ever. His deep black eyes were so calm, so penetrating, that instantly every head was uncovered. He had dressed with care and was the picture of health.

"I give no pledges," he said. "I make no intimations one way or the other; and I will be as free when this day closes, to act as duty calls, as I was when the dawn of this day . . ."

The cheering was so loud and incessant he had to pause in his talk. Only after several minutes was he able to resume:

". . . You know, gentlemen, that twenty years of honest and not altogether undistinguished service in the Whig cause did not save me from an outpouring of wrath which seldom proceeds from Whig presses and Whig tongues against anybody. I am, gentlemen, a little hard to coax; but as to being driven, that is out of the question . . ."

JOY AND SORROW

NOT UNTIL MAY OF THE FOLLOWING YEAR DID DANIEL Webster resign as Secretary of State in President Tyler's Cabinet. By then he felt he had done all he could for his country. Moreover, he was again in difficult financial straits.

During their years in Washington, after he bought the Swann house facing Lafayette Square, near the White House, his expenses had been enormous. He had often urged Caroline to indulge in fewer sumptuous entertainments; but he was as much at fault as she, for at Marshfield he kept open house; he even financially assisted many of his friends. He was particularly fond of country people and considered all his Green Harbor neighbors among his best friends.

But the upkeep of his two farms, which at this time were his only possessions, proved costly. It was essential that he return to the "everlasting company of plain-

147

tiff and defendant," as he humorously described his profession.

"Oh, Marshfield, and the sea, the sea!" Daniel kept saying to himself as he neared his Massachusetts estate.

He had added again and again to the original house. By now he had some two thousand acres of undulating land and five miles of seashore; the estate was almost baronial in its proportions.

The house was twice its original size; on the ground floor were nine handsomely furnished rooms opening into one another with spacious chambers above. At the west end was the new library which his daughter Julia had designed for him in neo-Gothic style. Large as this room was, it could not hold all his books; his agricultural and natural-history books were housed in a separate small building on the estate; his law library remained in Boston.

In addition to the main house, which had a porch running all around it, there were a couple of dozen other buildings on the grounds, including several fine barns, the gardener's cottage, the dairyman's cottage, the fisherman's house, the house of the chief tenant, and many others.

Marshfield was his home, where he felt he belonged. "The Elms," his childhood home in New Hampshire, was a second home; here he felt he belonged in a native sense. When momentarily free from the responsibilities of his country, he would stay first at one, then at the other of these country estates.

But now he was at the gates of Marshfield.

"Oh, Marshfield, and the sea, the sea!" he cried aloud as the boundless ocean came into view.

Fletcher, his elder son, was with Caleb Cushing in China, as Secretary to the Legation there; Edward, his younger son, was Secretary of the Commission for deciding the boundary of Canada; so neither of them was at Marshfield. But Julia and her children were awaiting him there, as was Fletcher's wife, Caroline, and their dear children, except for his darling granddaughter Grace—named for his own child. She, too, had died at an early age.

The morning after his arrival he awoke at dawn. He hastened from his chamber, down the stairs and through the other rooms, leaving all doors wide open behind him. He scarcely noticed Caroline's sleepy protests, as the brisk spring air reached her. She had been confined to bed with a cold when he arrived. But Daniel was convinced that fresh air was wholesome in sickness or in health.

Striding along, he raised his voice in song. It was good to be alive! It was ecstasy to be alive at Marshfield! There was no sight so inspiring, he thought, as to see the sun rise in all its majesty over the limitless sea!

How sweet, how fresh, how delightful was this early May morning in its cool stillness. The blossoming fruit trees stretched as far as eye could reach. In the early light they looked almost enchanted.

Creation breaking forth was as new as it had been to Adam, Daniel thought, as he strode along. It called all who had life and breath and being to a new adoration and a new gratitude. He was "as alone as Adam," at four in the morning, as he approached the Marshfield barns where his favorite cattle, who seemed to know and welcome him, were waiting to be fed.

After breakfast he sought out his old friend Seth Peterson. Spying Seth's wind-reddened face, he called loudly:

"What-ho, Commodore! Are the fish all set to bite?"

"Aye, Aye, sir," his old friend called back, as he approached him with his hands in the pockets of his old flannels, his faded shirt flapping about his arms.

Soon the two were off in Daniel's fishing smack, which he had named the *Seth Peterson*. It was a glorious day and they made a particularly good catch; but they overlooked the tide, which had gone before they could reach the dock. They stuck in the mud.

"Mr. Webster, if you'll get out and walk along the shore, the boat will be so much lighter I may be able to get her out."

"Well, Commodore, if you say so, I will. You are in command here."

So Daniel got out and walked. He stopped presently and looked back.

"Well, does she get along any?" he shouted at Peterson.

"Yes, yes, she gets on by hitches, as lawyers get to heaven," Seth replied without thinking. As soon as the words were out of his mouth he was appalled. He looked up, almost too frightened to see clearly.

There stood Daniel laughing heartily, his white teeth showing in the distance.

Luckily, thought Seth, Mr. Webster was a man who could always enjoy a joke at his own expense.

The following year the Whigs ignored Daniel and nominated Henry Clay for the Presidency. But he lost. The Democratic party won, and James K. Polk became the President. At this time a vacancy in the Senate occurred with the resignation of Rufus Choate. Daniel Webster was urged to fill it, and, as the Whigs had received him back in the fold, he felt obliged to consent.

The country at this time was in a state of agitation over the annexation of Texas, the Oregon boundary dispute, and the trouble with Mexico. Edward Webster had resigned his position to gather together a regiment of volunteers for the Mexican War, only to find that the President had changed his mind about wanting them.

Daniel had for many years been a constant and popular speaker at dinners and gatherings in various cities, towns, and villages throughout the country. He was as agitated as anyone over the Oregon boundary question, which threatened war with England, and over the Mexican trouble, which threatened war with Mexico.

In Philadelphia he suggested that the civilized world would not long countenance war to settle disputes, for might did not make right.

"The sense of modern times, the law of humanity, the honor of civilized states," he insisted, "all require that controversies of this sort, which cannot be adjusted by the parties themselves, should be referred to the decision of some intelligent and impartial tribunal."

One day in Boston Daniel called on his octogenarian friend, Jeremiah Mason, who had remained loyal to him during his difficulties with the Whigs. The talk turned to the Wilmot Proviso, which excluded slavery forever from all territory ceded by Mexico. It was the great question of the moment.

"I don't want to sound vain," Daniel told his old friend, "but the simple truth is that nearly a decade ago I committed myself to the whole doctrine fully and entirely."

"And now you find that Mr. Wilmot claims to be the discoverer of it?" Mason flashed a familiar glance from under his thick brows. "You find Mr. Wilmot has taken out a patent? I thought you were a more astute lawyer than to allow that, Daniel!"

"I must be permitted to say that I cannot quite consent to allowing the backers of this panacea to claim all the merit. I deny priority to their invention, sir! It is not their thunder!"

"I believe you, Daniel," Jeremiah Mason looked kindly at his former protégé. "You have always been a leader, far ahead of the crowd. So far ahead often that it will take a hundred years to catch up with you."

"That's not exactly encouraging, sir."

"No, it isn't. But that's why you were passed over for Henry Clay by the Whigs outside of New England and why you may be passed over again. It is the price a man pays who is in advance of his time."

"Exactly what are you referring to, Mr. Mason?"

"Specifically to your moderation. I see that you urged Philadelphians to turn their troubles over to an impartial tribunal, shunning war. Don't you know that all our Presidents get elected just because they are war heroes?" He smiled with affectionate familiarity at the younger man. "The military will never see eye to eye with men like us."

Nor did they. Soon General Scott was in Mexico City at the head of a victorious American Army!

Major Edward Webster had his chance at last. When a long period passed with no news of him, Daniel was not worried. No news was good news. Moreover, Henry Pleasants was with Edward and would look after the young Webster. Henry was an old and valued friend, a former slave, for whom Daniel had paid five hundred dollars and freed. When Henry left his family to accompany Edward to Mexico, Daniel had been moved to say that he had never spent his money more wisely!

While he longed for some word from Edward, Daniel also worried about Julia. His only and dearly beloved daughter was very ill. She had taken a severe cold in the early part of the winter, which developed latent tubercular tendencies. The disease made rapid progress. Daniel was so alarmed he urged his wife to leave him and go to Boston to be with Julia.

By Christmas Julia had recovered sufficiently to write him an amusing letter. "Sammy cried bitterly the day you left," she wrote. "I tried to divert his mind by talking of Christmas but he said 'All I want is grand-papa in my stocking.' Rather a capacious stocking would be required!"

Such happy jesting gave Daniel renewed confidence in Julia's recovery, and by the middle of February Julia appeared to be much better. Daniel was immensely relieved. He was full of cheerful plans for the coming spring when he unexpectedly received the news that his son, Edward, had died the last week in January.

Young Major Webster had entered Mexico City with the army. During the march the weather was extremely bad, a cold north wind blowing, and a heavy rain falling. Edward had been fourteen hours in the saddle, wet through to the skin, when he finally arrived in camp. Three weeks later he died of a fever. Henry Pleasants watched over him with constant care and affection, sitting by Edward's bedside when he died in his sleep. He was bringing Edward's body home on a favorite horse, which Edward, during his entire illness, had fed through an open window.

Daniel was stunned. He could scarcely believe the shocking news. Now he had only one son and one daughter left.

How hideous it was to outlive your own children, he thought, as he continued his lonely pacing up and down, up and down.

Almost at once Daniel learned that Julia had taken a sudden turn for the worse. He rushed to Boston.

The last day of her life came that week. He remained with her constantly, as did other members of her devoted family. Julia was thin and flushed, almost ethereal in appearance, but still young and lovely. She lay in agony at moments, but her cheerful, happy nature would reassert itself after each struggle for breath.

Finally, about eight in the evening, she said clearly: "Let me go, for the day breaketh . . ." and died.

It was a calm and serene death. Daniel was too moved to speak. Her husband was distraught. Caroline broke down entirely. She had loved Julia as her own daughter.

The funeral was on May day. Just before it started, word was brought to Daniel that the body of his son Edward had arrived.

Three days later Major Edward Webster was buried with military honors. A great concourse of people waited in reverent sympathy for the afflicted father. When Daniel appeared, they uncovered and followed his carriage to the church. The entire populace of Boston was greatly moved.

When Daniel returned home to Marshfield, he knew he was an old man. He was sixty-six.

"It is a sad thing to outlive our children. You are now my only son, my only child, Fletcher," he said to his son.

Fletcher was so moved he could not reply.

"I have looked on your mother's coffin and that of your little sister Grace and tiny brother Charles twice this week. Now they all rest together." Daniel sighed deeply. "May God enable me to sustain these overwhelming sorrows, and still bless His most Holy Name."

Fletcher was unable to utter a comforting word. The

overpowering sorrow of losing his only brother and
only sister at the same time left him speechless.

> "'Go, gentle spirit, to your destined rest:
>   While I reversed our nature's kindlier doom,
>   Pour forth a father's sorrow on your tomb.'"

Daniel repeated the three lines softly. Then he seemed
to fall into a musing half-sleep, but Fletcher noticed
that tears rolled down his wrinkled cheeks. He bowed
his head and wept, too.

Several days later, on a fine May morning, Fletcher
and his son, Daniel, Jr., with his wife Caroline, his step-
mother Caroline, and Julia's young daughter Caroline,
and her son Samuel, joined his father and the estate
agent, Porter Wright. Mr. Wright and Daniel in silence
planted two "weeping" elm trees in front of the Marshfield house.

"These are to be called Brother and Sister trees,
aren't they?" young Samuel asked. "They're for my
mother and uncle Edward," he added importantly.

"So they are," said Porter Wright, as he stomped the
ground around each tree to make sure it was planted
firmly.

Daniel turned to his only son and said gravely, "I
want you to care for these trees as long as you live, for
the sake of Julia and Edward."

As they all strolled slowly back to the house, Fletcher
noticed that his father had grown much older since his
recent sorrow.

CHAPTER NINETEEN

"I STAND ALONE"

DANIEL WEBSTER ROSE EARLY ON THE SEVENTH OF March, 1850. As he had told Caroline the evening before, he must make a reply to John C. Calhoun; he must make a speech on the Union and discharge a clear conscience.

He decided to take a walk in still-unawakened Washington. He found himself quoting aloud to the empty streets:

> " 'Never did sun more beautifully steep
> In his first splendor valley, rock, or hill;
> Ne'er saw I, never felt, a calm so deep!
> The river glideth at his own sweet will:
> Dear God! the very houses seem asleep;
> And all the mighty heart is lying still!' "

On his return he met Charles Brown, who had been in his employ for more than thirty years.

156

"Well, Charles, what's this I hear? So you've purchased a nice piece of ground and built yourself a comfortable home! Where did you get the money for so fine a house?"

"I am glad to say, sir, that it all came out of your pocket," replied his Negro friend whom he had emancipated many years before. "It was the money you gave me on holidays and other occasions."

"So that's how it is," replied Daniel, looking quizzically at his faithful friend. "I'm glad you're settled for life. I'm going to speak on the Union today. And no man knows where these violent controversies will lead."

"You lead those men, Mr. Webster, and I won't worry about where they're going!" was the admiring response.

Daniel Webster entered the breakfast room with a wry smile on his aging face. He must do his duty as he saw it, but what would be the response of the country?

He seemed again to hear his old friend Jeremiah Mason, who had now been dead over a year, saying, "It is your moderation." Jeremiah Mason had warned him he'd be passed over as a Presidential candidate. Well, he was right; General Zachary Taylor was the President. He, Daniel Webster, was still a member of the Senate, as he had been twenty years before.

Giants were in the Senate at this time: John C. Calhoun, who was a dying man; Henry Clay, who often ran for but never won the Presidency; Jefferson Davis, who later was to become the President of the Southern Confederacy; Stephen A. Douglas, Lincoln's opponent; Salmon P. Chase, later to be Chief Justice of the Supreme Court; William H. Seward, Secretary of State under Lincoln; Hannibal Hamlin, Vice-President with Lincoln; Thomas Hart Benton, leader of the Senate for thirty years; and Samuel Houston, hero of the battle of San Jacinto and leader of the Texans.

The floors, the galleries, the antechambers of the Senate were so densely crowded on this famous Seventh of March that these distinguished men and their colleagues found it difficult to enter and take their seats. Word had spread about that Daniel Webster was to speak!

Grave and dignified, he rose with commanding majesty, and turned his dark eyes upon the men, women and children crowding about him.

A wave of excitement ran through the gathered throng as he started to speak:

"I speak today for the preservation of the Union. 'Hear me for my cause.' I speak today, out of a solicitous and anxious heart, for the restoration to the country of that quiet and that harmony, which made the blessing of this Union so rich, so dear to us all . . ."

A deeper breathlessness held his listeners as he went on reviewing the history of slavery from the earliest times, explaining to a Louisiana Senator that he was foolish to imagine, as he had said, that "the absolute ignorance and abject slavery of the South was more in conformity with the high purposes and destiny of immortal and rational human beings than the educated, the independent, the free labor of the North . . ."

Every listener leaned forward in order not to miss a word of the deep voice.

"Secession. Peaceable secession! There can be no such thing as peaceable secession . . . No, sir. No, sir, I will not state what might produce the disruption of the Union, but, sir, I see so plainly as I see the sun in heaven what that disruption itself might produce: I see it must produce war, and such a war as I will not describe, in its two-fold character . . .

"Peaceable secession! Peaceable secession!" he continued. "What is to remain American? What am I to be? An American no longer? Am I to be a sectional man? . . . Where is the flag of the republic to remain? Where is the eagle still to tower? Or is it to cower and shrink and fall to the ground? What is to become of the army? What is to become of the navy? . . .

"It is supposed possible there will be a Southern Confederacy."

Gasps came from various sections of the chamber; the excitement increased.

"And, now, Mr. President, instead of speaking of the possibility or utility of secession, instead of dwelling in those caverns of darkness, instead of groping with those ideas full of all that is horrid and horrible, let us come out into the light of day . . ."

Daniel Webster had been speaking for many hours. But with these words, with this idea which was the core of his being, a radiance spread over his face, a refreshing vigor rejuvenated his body.

". . . let us enjoy the fresh air of Liberty and Union . . . let us not be pygmies in a case that calls for men . . .

"Never did there devolve on any generation of men higher trusts than now devolve upon us, for the preservation of this Constitution and the harmony and peace of all who are destined to live under it . . ."

He had almost reached the final words of his most famous oration, which he crowned with a Homeric quotation, describing the buckler of the hero Achilles:

"'Now the broad shield complete, the artist
    crowned
  With his last hand, and poured the ocean
    round;

In living silver seemed the waves to roll,
And beat the buckler's verge and bound the
    whole.'"

A deep sigh escaped his listeners; then came deafening applause. No speech in the Senate ever caused a
greater sensation.

Daniel Webster, now in his sixty-eighth year, had
spoken truly, as he believed. He had publicly proclaimed his love of the Union and of Liberty under
Law.

He was attacked violently in the North as well as in
the South. Extremists of both camps were enraged. In
both the North and the South men had voted for secession. In the January before this March, the Massachusetts Antislavery Society had held a meeting in Faneuil
Hall and resolved "That we seek a dissolution of the
Union."

The bloody conflict was already shaping itself; a
voice of reason could no longer be heard. On every
hand men were saying, "there is something higher than
the Constitution."

Many of Daniel's admirers and supporters in Massachusetts turned upon him: Ralph Waldo Emerson, the
essayist and philosopher; Theodore Parker, the divine;
John Greenleaf Whittier, the poet—all assailed Daniel.
They could not understand this man who held that
mind should be supreme over emotion.

Daniel agreed with his predecessor, the greatest pro-
pounder of the common law in England, Sir Edward
Coke, that "reason is the life of the law, the common
law itself is nothing else than reason . . . The law is
the perfection of reason."

He saw only too clearly that when lawless men break

down the dikes of reason, the flood of conflict pours over the unhappy land.

This tender-hearted, aging man was painfully hurt by the misunderstanding which his Seventh of March speech brought forth. When his New England colleagues turned on him, he was cut to the quick.

Only to his son Fletcher did he unburden himself.

"I regret that not one concurring vote can be found in all Massachusetts. I regret this much, but I hope I may be able to stand, though I stand alone," he said sadly. "At any rate, I shall stand till I fall. I will not sit down."

"I know, Father," Fletcher agreed. "You have been wholly misunderstood."

"My purpose was never to shut slavery out of the new Territories, nor to make every man in the North a slave-catcher, as one or the other side insists. Nor, of course, did I give a thought to the coming election."

Then, with unusual solemnity, Daniel added, "I sought a final and lasting settlement of a question which threatens the very life of our Union, which threatens to destroy our Constitution."

"Rufus Choate stands by you, Father. He understands." Fletcher was deeply moved. "You know well that Edward Everett and William M. Evarts would have you for the next Presidential candidate if they could. And President Fillmore has asked you to become Secretary of State. You will accept, won't you?" Fletcher asked, trying to turn his father's thoughts to the future.

"Probably. I believe it to be my duty to continue along the line from which I have never swerved since I first spelled out the Constitution from a cotton handkerchief. Whether the irritation can be lessened, whether reason can prevail, I do not know. But I do know that true patriotism is needed to carry us through these coming years."

He paused. "I mean to stand by the Constitution. I need no other platform. I shall know but *one* country, Fletcher, as I've ever known but *one*." His voice was soft, as if he were speaking of a dearly loved friend.

"As I've often said, the ends at which I aim shall always be my God's, my country's, and Truth's. No man can suffer too much, no man can fall too soon, if he suffer or if he fall in defense of the liberties and the Constitution of his country!"

"Here in Massachusetts they will live to repent of their short-sighted slander. I am sure of that, Father," his son spoke fervently. He had been shocked when such men as Emerson, Whittier, and Parker attacked his father. John C. Calhoun, a great man and a Southerner, had not been so stupid.

"Did I tell you, Father, I heard in Washington that Mr. Calhoun, just before his death, said: 'Mr. Webster has as high a standard of truth as any statesman with whom I have met in debate. Convince him, and he cannot reply; he is silent; he cannot look *truth* in the face and oppose it by argument!'"

During the next years as Secretary of State, Daniel spoke for Kossuth and Hungarian freedom; he addressed the New York Historical Society and various groups in the East.

Early in May he had a disagreeable accident. On a fine day he and his secretary, Charles Lanman, had set out for Plymouth in an old-fashioned phaeton with two horses. He was pointing out to his clerk the spot where the Mayflower landed, when suddenly a bolt connecting the front with the back wheels broke. The body of the open-front carriage fell to the ground, and Daniel was thrown into the road. He threw his hands and arms forward to protect his head; hence, his wrists and arms were seriously injured. It was a severe shock to the seventy-year-old man.

He was carried, covered with blood, into a neighboring house. Some days after, when he was left alone, he found he was unable to lift the door-latch or ring a bell. His arm was discolored and in a sling for some time. He was very weak.

Gradually he recovered enough to speak briefly in Faneuil Hall. Then he returned to his duties in Washington.

He was aging rapidly. When the Whigs again repudiated him at their Presidential Convention and chose General Scott, Daniel again thought wryly of his last conversation with Jeremiah Mason.

Daniel Webster was well along in his seventy-first year when, on a sultry July afternoon in Roxbury, Massachusetts, he entered a barouche drawn by six gray horses. He wore for the occasion a loose gray sack coat of fine cloth, lined with silk of the same color. As he entered the carriage, a discharge of cannon was answered by fieldpieces in the great square. At the same time all the bells of Roxbury and Boston began to ring.

At an early hour of the afternoon, shops and stores had begun to close; the city put on an air of a national holiday. All streets were lined with multitudes of people; many strangers had come in on the crowded trains throughout the day. The streets were decorated, gay with flags and patriotic banners. Portraits of Daniel Webster hung on the balconies and walls of the houses.

As the concourse went through Washington, Tremont, and West Bedford to Daniel's house on Summer

Street, Daniel could scarcely control himself. A stream of past events flooded his memory: Here he had lived with Grace—tender, understanding Grace. No man had ever had a sweeter wife, no children a more devoted mother. He could close his eyes and see Julia coming home from a party, a young girl, graceful and lovely in her happy innocence. It was here his sons had spent their boyhood. From here Edward had gone to his eternal rest. Edward . . . he couldn't think of Edward without tears.

Daniel turned his face toward the State Street decorations, glad they had traversed Summer Street and Washington and were again on the return route. Everywhere, as far as his eye could reach, thousands had come out to do him honor. Women held up their children for a glance at the great man.

The crowd cheered wildly, and soon the "three cheers" merged into one loud roar. His carriage was filled with bouquets of flowers; the streets were strewn with flower garlands. Hundreds of happy faces were turned toward the old man. Women waved from every window; handkerchiefs fluttered even from housetops. The streets were filled with people of all ages, of all political parties, of all faiths—one and all out to honor Daniel Webster.

At the Charles Street Gate, the procession paused. They had reached the Boston Common. Daniel Webster, accompanied by important persons, entered the gate.

The amphitheatre made an impressive scene. Along the base of the hill the troops were drawn up in serried lines. The crowd of men, women and children extended to the top of the hill. As soon as the military salutes were completed, the crowd pressed around the platform, eager to hear the great statesman's every word.

Daniel was accustomed to facing huge and eager audiences. But today he was very tired. He was an old man and not a well man. But he rallied his strength. He must not disappoint his fellow Americans. A great love for his city, his state, and his whole country filled his heart. This popular demonstration, honoring him, touched him deeply. It was these people he loved—the common people of his country.

What was Mr. Stevenson saying?

"Justice to a patriot is justice to the people . . . No party bugle has sounded a call for this gathering. All that has been done was to notify the public of the opportunity. See how the public has seized it! We all welcome you, it is a hundred thousand welcomes!"

How kind, how very kind, thought Daniel. He spoke briefly, due to his great fatigue. The short address ended with the words:

"You know, gentlemen, it is not my fortune to be or to have been a successful military chieftain. I am nothing but a painstaking, hard-working civilian, giving my life and my health and my strength to the maintenance of the Constitution; and the upholding, according to the best of my ability, under the Providence of God, of the liberties of my country."

CHAPTER TWENTY

"KEEP MY LIGHT BURNING"

A FEW DAYS LATER DANIEL WEBSTER, ACCOMPANIED by his clerk, Charles Lanman, took a train for New Hampshire. As always in recent years, crowds gathered to see him at Lowell, Nashua, Manchester, and Hooksett. At Concord, where they left the train, the crowds were even larger; but Daniel was too tired to say more than a few words to anyone.

When they reached "Elms Farm" Daniel hastened to the home of his agent, John Taylor, who had been gored by a bull. Carrying the packages of fresh salmon and baskets of grapes Daniel had brought from Boston, the two men were greeted at the cottage door by Mr. Taylor's son, a boy of twelve.

"How is your father today?" Daniel inquired, while Charles Lanman entered the house with the gifts.

"He's more comfortable, sir."

"Exactly what happened?" asked Daniel. "I've been greatly distressed by the news of his accident."

"You see, sir, I was friends with St. Stephen and he knew me. I always led him to the water to drink and took him around the field for exercise. We were friends, you see."

Daniel smiled to himself. So the enormous Hungarian bull and this young farmer boy were friends!

"Well, my boy, if St. Stephen is such an amiable animal why did he attack your father?"

"Father says he was afraid of him and St. Stephen knew it," explained the youngster. "Perhaps it hurt St. Stephen's feelings."

"Um . . ." Daniel gazed gravely at the small figure. It reminded him of his own youth and of Zeke. Zeke had been fearless in just this natural manner. For an instant Daniel felt as if Zeke were actually by his side. He went on questioning the Taylor boy.

"Father sent me away; it wasn't my fault, sir," the boy explained. "It must have been awful. St. Stephen put one of his horns right through my father's thigh and tossed him into the air!"

"Your father is a very brave man," Daniel said. "I understand he fell violently on his back, but while the bull trampled him he clung to the rope until he could reach the ring in the great animal's nose."

"That's right, sir. Father was gored and trampled badly, but the doctor says he'll get well. He will, won't he, sir? I wouldn't want St. Stephen to be a murderer!"

How fond the boy was of the bull! Daniel understood this deep love of the majestic animal. He himself was devoted to the great creatures.

When Charles Lanman came outside and announced that the old man was sleeping, they returned to the big house. Daniel was so tired that he sank into his chair and closed his eyes.

Sometime later he gazed out of the north and east windows. In the distance the Merrimac flowed by, just as it had in his youth. By this time the river had so deepened its channel that it was invisible from the house. But he knew it was there and in his imagination he saw it plainly.

When the railroad took a path through the old barns, Daniel had been afraid he would have to move the big house, but he had finally decided to make the best of the occasional noise and dirt rather than change the site of his boyhood home.

From the east windows his eyes swept over a level field of some hundred acres, with spreading elms and maples in full leaf; lambs were cropping the grass. How often he and Zeke had run barefoot over this very field. Again his brother seemed vividly before him. He passed his hand over his eyes.

At the end of the field he saw the plain marble gravestones of his entire family. Not only his mother and father, but his sisters with their good scriptural names—Mehitable, Abigail, and Sarah—were there.

He remembered his father's stories of revolutionary valor, and recalled the part Lafayette had played in the fight for freedom. Daniel smiled, thinking of the Boston tribute to Lafayette, more than thirty years before, when he had made his oration on Bunker Hill.

How odd it seemed that his recent reception should have far out-distanced the one to the hero of the Revolution! If only Zeke could have lived to see it! If only his father could have known whether Daniel had come to something or nothing!

After a few days' rest on the old farm, Daniel felt more vigorous. It had been far from a complete rest, for his friends and neighbors came daily in large numbers for assistance or advice. Grace, dear, dear Grace and Zeke, handsome, magnificent Zeke, were the constant companions of his silent thought.

When Fletcher arrived with young Daniel Webster, Jr., the statesman was struck by Fletcher's resemblance to his mother. His grave eyes were the same blue-gray, clear and cool, and he had her spontaneous smile. The young boy looked more like Daniel himself. He was very proud of this third Daniel Webster.

The three of them went to see John Taylor, who was now convalescing. Young Daniel hurried off to accompany the Taylor boy with his farm chores, while Daniel and Fletcher conversed with Mr. Taylor.

Presently Taylor declared: "I have a very bad opinion of that bull. Why, Mr. Webster, he is no more fit to be at large than Mr. Kossuth is!"

His visitors burst into laughter.

"These Hungarian cattle," Fletcher announced in a mock-serious voice, "biped or quadruped, are dangerous to American institutions and constitutions!"

The three men laughed heartily.

"That's the living truth," agreed John Taylor. "Full and complete."

After more talk about animals and farming conditions, Daniel announced: "An artist is coming down from Boston to make some pictures of that bull; a bull that can throw such a man as you, John Taylor, is an animal, indeed!"

"You'll be welcome to the pictures," retorted Taylor. "I have no desire to remember that bull!"

"But I shall give one to your son," insisted Daniel. "He told me St. Stephen was his best friend."

"Father," said Fletcher in a teasing manner, as they were walking back to the house, "do you think John

Taylor will appreciate your winning his son to the Hungarian cause?"

"And why not?" asked Daniel. "It's the same cause for freedom your grandfather fought for! Mr. Kossuth is a poet, not a sound reasoner, but he as sincerely loves his country as our patriots did."

Fletcher noticed that the grave, sedate man at his side was looking tired. He knew the threat to the New England fisheries was weighing on him. His clerk had been getting off letters to President Fillmore all morning.

The matter of the squadrons sent from England to exclude American fishermen had reached a serious stage. It was all due to an oversight on the part of the United States in the Convention of 1818. Mr. Crampton had come from England, and Daniel planned to receive him at Marshfield. While Daniel remained Secretary of State he intended to keep England and America on friendly terms.

Daniel spent several days in Boston before he was at last free to go to Marshfield the final week of July.

When he hurried off the train at Kingston, nine miles away, he was met by a large gathering of his neighbors and people from the surrounding country. There were more than one hundred and fifty vehicles, as well as many on horseback and on foot. They had come to escort Daniel Webster home.

The people had not intended to go into the Marshfield grounds but Daniel insisted.

"They *must* go. I don't care if they tear up the avenues and grounds six feet deep," Daniel was emphatic. "These people all want to go to the house and they *must* go."

It was a spontaneous, hearty reception; the procession was two miles long. The roads were lined with women and children, and the pathway was covered with flowers.

When they reached the high ground, where a platform had been erected, one of his neighbors spoke:

". . . We hope you may live long to teach us the art of using the ploughshare instead of the sword, and the pruning-hook rather than the spear."

Exhausted as he was, Daniel responded with sympathy to these neighbors and friends. Some listeners detected a note of sadness in his words. It was sunset when he finished speaking.

He entered his home at last and threw himself into a chair. Slowly he looked up and saw the portrait of his dearly beloved daughter, Julia. He gazed at the picture a long time; then suddenly he burst into tears.

"Oh, I am so thankful to be here!" he cried, as if in pain. "If I could only have my will, never, never, would I again leave this house."

A few days later Daniel was back at work on government affairs. He made brief journeys to Boston and to Washington. In the latter place he spent some time with President Fillmore.

Before he left the city, a friend told him a delightful story about the President. It seemed that when Fillmore became President on the death of Taylor, his eighty-year-old father came to visit. After a week he packed his bag and started to leave. A White House visitor suggested he remain longer. "No, no, sir," the old man replied, "I will go. I don't like it here; it isn't a good place to live. It isn't a good place for Millard. I wish he was at home in Buffalo."

Despite his genuine liking of the President, Daniel could heartily agree with Fillmore's old father. He, too, was anxious to be back at Marshfield for good.

By early fall Daniel Webster had become very ill.

"Are you feeling better today?" a guest asked anxiously.

"I'm not good for much. My strength is nearly gone," Daniel answered quietly. "I'm scarcely a match for my own grandson these days."

That evening he was too tired to play his usual game of whist. He retired early, before tea had been brought to the library. Only one lamp had as yet been lighted.

Suddenly he reappeared among his guests, dressed in his blue overcoat. He was followed by William Johnson, a former slave whom Daniel had bought and freed. William was carrying a pail of milk, which Daniel had him place on the library writing-table. Everyone gathered around.

"Light the candles, William," Daniel said, "and place them close to the pail, so everyone can see with what fine, rich milk my favorite Alderney supplies me."

His guests realized that Daniel was momentarily revived by his interest in his farm. And the next morning, as his friends were leaving, he said:

"I mean to be a sportsman and a farmer, to go out on the waters for fish and go shooting next week. There'll be no gentleman at the head of the house to receive the guests."

His illness, however, took a turn for the worse. He was confined to the house and endured sleepless nights.

After one such night of pain, he walked down to the windows at the front of the house, and watched Porter Wright drive a herd of his best oxen over the lawn. It gave him strength to look at the great animals cropping the grass.

He kept a boat on the largest pond of the estate, which was close to the house. A pole stood in place of the mast; from its summit a small United States flag waved in the autumn breeze.

"I love to distinguish those bright and beautiful stripes in the first dawn of morning," Daniel said.

While Caroline was occupied, he called in one of his farm helpers. "You must go and get a nice ship-lantern," he said, "and trim it." After a pause he added, "I want this to be a secret. At six o'clock this evening I want it there. But no one must know." Daniel's black eyes twinkled with glee.

That evening the man returned and said, "Mr. Webster, there's a flock of geese on the pond. Come and see them."

Daniel realized the man meant the lantern was ready, so he turned to Caroline, who was sitting beside him, and said: "My dear, he says there's a flock of geese on the pond. Come and see them."

"It seems to me you're very childish, Daniel," she replied. But she went with him to the window.

"Why, my dear, your boat's on fire!" Caroline exclaimed.

"That's the flock of geese," Daniel explained, smiling merrily at his helper.

"I want you to trim the lantern and put it up at six o'clock every evening and take it down at six o'clock each morning—as long as I live," Daniel said gravely. "It will comfort me when I do not sleep to look out and see it there."

He paused. Then added with spirit: "Keep my light burning!"

About the beginning of the fourth week of October,

he was urged to make an announcement in favor of the Whig Presidential candidate, General Scott, to whom he had been opposed since the first.

"They want a statement as to where you stand," a friend insisted.

A smile spread over Daniel's tired old face. "Tell them to take a look at the Bunker Hill Monument," Daniel said, with the familiar twinkle in his eye.

Then he turned to the friend at his bedside who had just completed drawing up his will.

"I care no more about politics than the jackdaw that sits on the top of St. Paul's. Go down into my library and read about that sensible bird," suggested Daniel. Then he quoted from the poet Cowper:

> "'You think, no doubt, he sits and muses
>   On future broken bones and bruises,
>   If he should chance to fall.
>   No; not a single thought like that
>   Employs his philosophic pate,
>   Or troubles it at all.

> "'He sees that this great roundabout,
>   The world with all its motley rout,
>   Church, army, physic, law,
>   Its custom and its businesses,
>   Is no concern at all of his;
>   And says—what says he?—Caw!'"

Each night Daniel became worse. When the final day of his life dawned, he recognized it as such. He took affectionate farewells of his family and servants, trying with his calmness to sustain them in their sorrow.

He began to repeat the Lord's Prayer but after a few words he grew faint. "Hold me up. I do not wish to pray with a fainting voice," he implored. "Peace on earth and good will to men—that is the happiness, the essence—good will towards men," he said, and lapsed into unconsciousness.

Monica, his cook whom he had purchased from an unkind master and freed over thirty years before, could not restrain her emotion. She wandered about his room, muttering snatches of prayers.

Everyone wept.

His youngest grandson, Peter Harvey Webster, Fletcher's son, was awed into frightened silence by the scene.

"I still live!" Daniel cried. "I live . . . poetry . . ."

He looked anxiously at Fletcher, who had not left his bedside. Gently and clearly Fletcher repeated from memory the lines his father loved, by the poet Gray:

" 'The curfew tolls the knell of parting day,
    The lowing herd winds slowly o'er the lea,
The plowman homeward plods his weary way,
    And leaves the world to darkness and to me.

" 'Now fades the glimmering landscape on the sight,
    And all the air a solemn stillness holds,
Save where the beetle wheels his droning flight,
    And drowsy tinklings lull the distant folds.

.   .   .

" 'Let not Ambition mock their useful toil,
    Their homely joys, and destiny obscure;
Nor grandeur hear with a disdainful smile
    The short and simple annals of the poor.' "

Before Fletcher could quote another verse, Daniel Webster, noble and true to the last, had fallen into eternal sleep.

A few days later his coffin was placed on the lawn in front of his Marshfield home. A brilliant October sun poured down; the trees and foliage were in their autumnal glory of yellow, red, and brown.

Thousands came to pay their final tribute to a great man. All classes, all ages, the rich, the poor, the educated, the uneducated, the farmer, the mechanic, the professor, the lawyer, the politician; from far and near they came.

In this immense crowd was an unknown man in rustic garb, who looked at Daniel for the last time and said:

"Daniel Webster, the world, without you, will seem lonesome."